Core Books in Advanced Mathematics

This book is to
the last da

Probability

Core Books in Advanced Mathematics

General Editor: C. PLUMPTON, Moderator in Mathematics,
University of London School Examinations Department;
formerly Reader in Engineering Mathematics,
Queen Mary College, University of London.

Titles available
Statistics
Probability
Methods of Algebra
Differentiation
Integration
Vectors
Curve Sketching
Newton's Laws and Particle Motion
Mechanics of Groups of Particles
Methods of Trigonometry
Coordinate Geometry and Complex Numbers
Proof

Core Books in Advanced Mathematics

Probability

P. Sabine
Chief Examiner in Advanced Level Mathematics,
University of London School Examinations Department;
formerly Lecturer in Mathematics and Statistics,
Chelsea College, University of London.

C. Plumpton
Moderator in Mathematics,
University of London School Examinations Department;
formerly Reader in Engineering Mathematics,
Queen Mary College, University of London.

M

Macmillan Education
London and Basingstoke

First published 1985

Published by
MACMILLAN EDUCATION LTD
Houndmills, Basingstoke, Hampshire RG21 2XS
and London
Companies and representatives
throughout the world

Printed in Hong Kong

British Library Cataloguing in Publication Data
Sabine, P.
Probability.——(Core books in advanced
mathematics)
1. Probabilities
I. Title   II. Plumpton, C.   III. Series
519.2   QA273
ISBN 0–333–38363–X

Contents

Preface   vii

1   The laws of probability   1
Introduction; The multiplication law; Tree diagrams and Bayes' theorem;
Markov chains

2   Probability distributions   21
Random variables; Discrete probability distributions; Continuous
probability distributions

3   Some discrete probability distributions   35
Introduction; The discrete uniform distribution; The binomial
distribution; The geometric distribution; The Poisson distribution

4   Some continuous probability distributions   49
The continuous uniform distribution; The exponential distribution;
The normal distribution

Answers   73

Index   77

Preface

Advanced level mathematics syllabuses are once again undergoing changes of content and approach, following the revolution in the early 1960s which led to the unfortunate dichotomy between 'modern' and 'traditional' mathematics. The current trend in syllabuses for Advanced level mathematics now being developed and published by many GCE Boards is towards an integrated approach, taking the best of the topics and approaches of the modern and traditional, in an attempt to create a realistic examination target, through syllabuses which are maximal for examining and minimal for teaching. In addition, resulting from a number of initiatives, core syllabuses are being developed for Advanced level mathematics syllabuses, consisting of techniques of pure mathematics as taught in schools and colleges at this level.

The concept of a core can be used in several ways, one of which is mentioned above, namely the idea of a core syllabus to which options such as theoretical mechanics, further pure mathematics and statistics can be added. The books in this series are core books involving a different use of the core idea. They are books on a range of topics, each of which is central to the study of Advanced level mathematics; they form small core studies of their own, of topics which together cover the main areas of any single-subject mathematics syllabus at Advanced level.

Particularly at times when economic conditions make the problems of acquiring comprehensive textbooks giving complete syllabus coverage acute, schools and colleges and individual students can collect as many of the core books as they need, one or more, to supplement books already acquired, so that the most recent syllabuses of, for example, the London, Cambridge, JMB and AEB GCE Boards, can be covered at minimum expense. Alternatively, of course, the whole set of core books gives complete syllabus coverage of single-subject Advanced level mathematics syllabuses.

The aim of each book is to develop a major topic of the single-subject syllabuses, giving essential book work and worked examples and exercises arising from the authors' vast experience of examining at this level, and also including actual past GCE questions. Thus, the core books, as well as being suitable for use in either of the above ways, are ideal for supplementing comprehensive textbooks in the sense of providing more examples and exercises so necessary for preparation and revision for examinations on the Advanced level mathematics syllabuses offered by the GCE Boards.

An attempt has been made to give a readable yet mathematically accurate explanation of the concepts involved in the work on basic probability, many of which are first introduced by means of an example. A wide selection of examples for the reader to work is included at the end of each chapter, and, after each major topic, both worked examples and graded examples on that topic for the reader are provided.

A knowledge of elementary calculus is required for Chapters 2 and 4, which contain work on continuous variables, and for certain portions of Chapters 2 and 3 the ability to sum simple finite and infinite series is necessary.

Peggy Sabine
Charles Plumpton

1 The laws of probability

1.1 Introduction

Let us start by considering two questions:

(i) I have drawn a card from a well-shuffled pack. Is it a spade?

(ii) What is the chance that when I draw a card from a well-shuffled pack, it will be a spade?

The first of these questions cannot be answered with certainty without picking up the drawn card and looking at it, and we can then only give the answer 'Yes' or 'No', whichever is true. To the second question, using ideas of probability, we can give at any time a precise numerical answer built on mathematical foundations. Thus probability deals with problems of the type 'What is the chance that' some event happens, and the answer, in general, will be a numerical quantity (the probability). A scale of measurement is necessary, and the scale we use allows probabilities to be measured from 0 (impossibility) to 1 (certainty). An example of the former would be the probability that you will live for ever, and of the latter the probability that the sun will rise and set tomorrow.

In practice, the probability that it is impossible for something to happen, or for it to be certain to happen, is fairly rare, and most probabilities will lie between the values 0 and 1. However, some, such as the probability of winning the football pools, may be so small as to be approximately zero (but not actually equal to 0), and others may be very close to 1.

To return to our initial question (ii), the pack is well shuffled so that each card has an *equal chance* of being picked. There are 52 cards in the pack, of which 13 are spades; so there is a chance of 13 out of 52 that the card picked will be a spade. That is, there is a chance of 1 in 4, or a probability of $\frac{1}{4}$, that the card will be a spade. What, then, is the probability that the card will not be a spade? There are 39 cards which are not spades, and so the probability is $\frac{39}{52}$, or $\frac{3}{4}$. Denoting 'probability that the card is a spade' by P(S) and 'probability that the card is not a spade' by P(S'), we see that

$$P(S) + P(S') = 1 \text{ (certainty)},$$

an obvious result, since it is certain that either a spade or not a spade will be picked. The event S' is called the *complement* of the event S.

We call the act of picking a card an *experiment*; and the results of such picking, the possible *outcomes* or *simple events*. The set of all possible outcomes of an experiment is the *sample* (or *outcome*) *space*; this may be either *discrete*, when the simple events can be arranged as a sequence, or *continuous*, when the simple events are recorded on a continuous scale. For example, the experiment of counting the number of broken eggs in a case of 100 eggs will have the discrete sample space {0, 1, 2, ..., 100}; for the experiment of measuring the height of the surface of a river above or below a given mark, the sample space is continuous and is a portion of the real line. For the present, we restrict ourselves to problems in which the sample space is discrete. To each sample point of a finite sample space we have a corresponding probability, and these probabilities define a *probability function*. When a fair die (die is the singular of dice) is thrown, each of the outcomes 1, 2, 3, 4, 5, 6 has a probability of $\frac{1}{6}$ and the probability function is

$$P(r) = \frac{1}{6}, \quad r = 1, 2, \ldots, 6.$$

We can now generalise the result $P(S) + P(S') = 1$ which we found for the card example. Given that E is an event and denoting by E' the event that E does not happen, then

$$P(E) + P(E') = 1.$$

From the card example we can formulate a method of calculating simple probabilities. Given that E is the set of outcomes (all equally likely to occur) of an experiment, and given that another event F is satisfied by a subset F of E, then the probability of event F, $P(F)$, is given by

$$P(F) = \frac{n(F)}{n(E)} = \frac{\text{number of 'successful' outcomes}}{\text{total number of possible outcomes}}.$$

For a very simple example, as we saw, we can just write down $n(F)/n(E)$ — in our case $\frac{13}{52}$ — but in more complicated problems we may decide to find $n(F)$ and $n(E)$ by using permutations or combinations or both.

Sometimes, instead of stating the probability of an event happening, we state the *odds* of it happening. When we say that the odds are 1 to 2 that an event E will happen, we mean that $P(E) = \frac{1}{3}$. When we say that the *odds against E* happening are n to 1, we mean that $P(E') = n/(n + 1)$ and $P(E) = 1/(n + 1)$.

Example 1　From a group of 3 boys and 2 girls we wish to select 3 *at random* (that is, each of the 5 has an equal chance of being chosen) to organise a school sports day. Find the probability that there will be 1 and only 1 girl among the 3.

Total number of ways of choosing 3 out of 5 $= \dbinom{5}{3} = 10.$

Number of ways of choosing 1 girl $= 2.$

Number of ways of choosing 2 boys $= \binom{3}{2} = 3$.

$\Rightarrow$ Number of ways of choosing 1 girl and 2 boys $= 2 \times 3 = 6$.

$\Rightarrow$ Probability of 1 and only 1 girl in the chosen 3 $= \frac{6}{10} = \frac{3}{5}$.

We have mentioned already, both in the card problem and in the last example, the assumption of 'equally likely events'. This assumption must, of course, be justified when we are calculating probabilities, and if we take the probability of getting any number from 1 to 6 (inclusive) when we throw a die to be $\frac{1}{6}$, then we are assuming that the die is fair or *unbiased* and that each of the numbers 1 to 6 has an *equal chance* of occurring. Similarly, for a fair coin the probability of getting a 'head' in a toss is $\frac{1}{2}$, since there are 2 possible outcomes (each equally likely, if the coin is a fair one) of which 1 is a 'head'. Unless stated to the contrary, in this book all coins and dice are taken to be fair (unbiased), and packs of cards are normal packs of 52 cards.

Most problems in probability are concerned with the happening not of one event only but of two or more. Two events E and F are said to be *mutually exclusive* if they cannot occur together — that is, if $P(E \cap F) = 0$. For example, a 'head' and a 'tail' are mutually exclusive events when a coin is tossed.

In the card problem, suppose we wish to find the probability of getting a spade (S) or a heart (H).

$$P(S \cup H) = \frac{n(S \cup H)}{52} = \frac{26}{52} = \frac{1}{2},$$

since 26 cards are either spades or hearts, and

$$P(S \cup H \cup D) = \frac{39}{52} = \frac{3}{4},$$

since 39 cards are spades or hearts or diamonds (D). We see, then, that for the mutually exclusive events 'spade', 'heart', 'diamond', we have

$$P(S \cup H) = P(S) + P(H),$$
$$P(S \cup H \cup D) = P(S) + P(H) + P(D).$$

This suggests an *addition law* for probabilities. The general form of the law for two events E and F is

$$P(E \cup F) = P(E) + P(F) - P(E \cap F).$$

This can best be illustrated by using a Venn diagram (Fig. 1.1). E and F are subsets of S, the outcome space. We require

$$P(E \cup F) = \frac{n(E \cup F)}{n(S)} = \frac{n(E) + n(F) - n(E \cap F)}{n(S)},$$

since the subset $(E \cap F)$ shaded is included twice in $n(E) + n(F)$, and, hence,

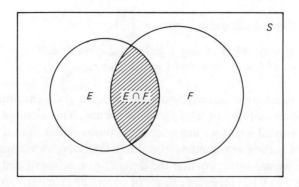

Fig. 1.1

$$P(E \cup F) = P(E) + P(F) - P(E \cap F).$$

Now if E and F are mutually exclusive events, then $P(E \cap F) = 0$, and, hence, the law becomes

$$P(E \cup F) = P(E) + P(F),$$

as was illustrated by our card example.

The events E_1, E_2, ..., E_n are said to be *exhaustive* if they cover all possible outcomes of an experiment; that is, the n events form the outcome space. In general, if E_1, E_2, ..., E_n are mutually exclusive events and they are also exhaustive, then we can extend the addition law to obtain

$$P(E_1 \cup E_2 \cup \ldots \cup E_n) = P(E_1) + P(E_2) + \ldots + P(E_n) = 1.$$

Example 2 A boy has 12 coins in his pocket — three 10p pieces, three 2p, one 1p, five 5p. He draws a coin at random from his pocket. Find the probability that it is
(a) either a 2p or a 10p coin,
(b) a 2p, a 5p or a 10p coin.

Here the events '2p', '5p', '10p', '1p' are mutually exclusive.

$$P(10p) = \frac{3}{12} = \frac{1}{4}, \quad P(2p) = \frac{1}{4}, \quad P(1p) = \frac{1}{12}, \quad P(5p) = \frac{5}{12}.$$

(Note here that the sum of all these probabilities must, and does, equal 1, certainty.)

(a) $P(2p \cup 10p) = P(2p) + P(10p) = \dfrac{1}{4} + \dfrac{1}{4} = \dfrac{1}{2}.$

(b) $P(2p \cup 5p \cup 10p) = P(2p) + P(5p) + P(10p) = \dfrac{1}{4} + \dfrac{5}{12} + \dfrac{1}{4} = \dfrac{11}{12}.$

Or, better, $P(2p \cup 5p \cup 10p) = 1 - P(1p) = 1 - \dfrac{1}{12} = \dfrac{11}{12}.$

Example 3 From a well-shuffled pack of cards one is picked at random. Find the probability that it is either a spade or a king.

Here the events 'spade' (S) and 'king' are not mutually exclusive, since they can occur together as the king of spades.

$$P(S) = \frac{13}{52} = \frac{1}{4}, \quad P(\text{king}) = \frac{4}{52} = \frac{1}{13}, \quad P(S \cap \text{king}) = \frac{1}{52}.$$

Hence, $P(S \cup \text{king}) = \frac{1}{4} + \frac{1}{13} - \frac{1}{52} = \frac{4}{13}$.

(Alternatively, we could say that the total number of cards that are either spade or king is 13 spades plus 3 other kings — that is, 16 cards in all. Hence, $P(S \cup \text{king}) = \frac{16}{52} = \frac{4}{13}$, as before.)

Example 4 Three items are chosen at random from a lot containing 16 items, of which 4 are defective. Find the probability that
(a) all three items are defective,
(b) all three items are non-defective,
(c) at least one item is defective.

The number of ways of choosing 3 items from 16 items is

$$\binom{16}{3} = \frac{16 \times 15 \times 14}{1 \times 2 \times 3} = 560 \text{ ways.}$$

(a) The number of ways of choosing 3 defective items from 4 defective items is

$$\binom{4}{3} = 4 \text{ ways.}$$

$\Rightarrow$ Probability that all 3 items are defective $= \dfrac{4}{560} = \dfrac{1}{140}$.

(b) The number of ways of choosing 3 non-defective items from 12 non-defective items is

$$\binom{12}{3} = \frac{12 \times 11 \times 10}{1 \times 2 \times 3} = 220 \text{ ways.}$$

$\Rightarrow$ Probability that all 3 items are non-defective $= \dfrac{220}{560} = \dfrac{11}{28}$.

(c) The event that at least 1 item is defective is the complement of the event that all 3 items are non-defective and, hence,

$$P(\text{all 3 items non-defective}) + P(\text{at least 1 item defective}) = 1.$$

$\Rightarrow P(\text{at least 1 item defective}) = 1 - \dfrac{11}{28} = \dfrac{17}{28}$.

Exercise 1.1

1 A die is weighted so that, when the die is thrown, a '6' is twice as likely to occur as each of the other numbers. Find the probability of a '6', and of each of the other numbers, occurring.

2 For the die of question 1, find the probability of obtaining on a single throw
   (a) an even number,
   (b) an odd number,
   (c) a prime number,
   (d) an odd prime number,
   (e) an even number which is not a prime number. [Treat '1' as prime.]

3 The events E and F are such that

$$P(E') = \tfrac{3}{4}, \quad P(E \cap F) = \tfrac{1}{5}, \quad P(E \cup F) = \tfrac{2}{3}.$$

Find
   (a) $P(E)$, (b) $P(F)$, (c) $P(E \cap F')$.

4 A committee of 3 is chosen at random from a group of 20 people consisting of 12 men and 8 women. Find the probability that
   (a) 3 men are chosen,
   (b) at least 1 man is chosen.

1.2 The multiplication law

We said that, for two mutually exclusive events E and F, $P(E \cap F) = 0$ by definition. The multiplication law enables us to find an expression for $P(E \cap F)$ when E and F are not mutually exclusive. Consider first the case where E and F are *independent events* — that is, where the knowledge of the occurrence of one event does not affect the probability of the other event occurring. Under this condition the probability that both E and F occur simultaneously is equal to the product of the probabilities that E and F occur separately — that is,

$$P(E \cap F) = P(E) . P(F).$$

(This can be extended to more than two independent events:

$$P(E \cap F \cap G) = P(E) . P(F) . P(G), \text{ etc.)}$$

For such independent events we could write

$$P(E, \text{ given that } F \text{ occurred}) = P(E)$$

and

$$P(F, \text{ given that } E \text{ occurred}) = P(F).$$

We use the symbol $|$ to shorten this and write

$$P(E|F) = P(E), \quad P(F|E) = P(F),$$

where E and F are independent events. $P(E|F)$ is called the *conditional probability* of E on F, and is to be read as the probability of E given that F has occurred. We can illustrate this by means of another Venn diagram (Fig. 1.2).

We will denote the sample space by S, and represent the set of equally likely outcomes of event E and the set of equally likely outcomes of event F within S as shown. Then $P(E|F)$ is the probability of E occurring given that F has occurred and, hence, the sample space is reduced to the set F.

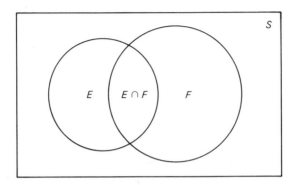

Fig. 1.2

Therefore

$$P(E|F) = \frac{n(E \cap F)}{n(F)} = \frac{n(E \cap F)}{n(S)} \cdot \frac{n(S)}{n(F)} = \frac{n(E \cap F)}{n(S)} \bigg/ \frac{n(F)}{n(S)} = \frac{P(E \cap F)}{P(F)}$$

or

$$P(E \cap F) = P(E|F).P(F) = P(F|E).P(E),$$

by symmetry. This is the *multiplication* rule. If E and F are independent events, we know that $P(E|F) = P(E)$ and the rule reduces, for independent events, to $P(E \cap F) = P(E).P(F)$, as stated earlier.

Example 5   A fair coin is tossed twice. Find the probability of obtaining exactly one 'tail'.

$$P(H) = \frac{1}{2}, \quad P(T) = \frac{1}{2}.$$ Events are independent.

$$\Rightarrow P(HT) = P(H).P(T) = \frac{1}{2}.\frac{1}{2} = \frac{1}{4},$$

$$P(TH) = P(T).P(H) = \frac{1}{4},$$

$$\Rightarrow P(\text{exactly one 'tail'}) = \frac{1}{4} + \frac{1}{4} = \frac{1}{2}.$$

Example 6   Data on heights of 930 mothers of only sons and their adult sons are given below. Heights for short and tall are divided at 1.57 m for mothers and 1.75 m for sons.

| | Son | | |
		Short	Tall	Total
Mother	Short	320	104	424
	Tall	180	326	506
	Total	500	430	(930)

Find the probability that
(a) a tall mother (TM) has a tall son (TS),
(b) a short mother (SM) has a tall son,
(c) a tall son has a short mother.

Here the events tall or short, mother or son, are not independent.

(a) $P(TS|TM) = \dfrac{P(TS \cap TM)}{P(TM)} = \dfrac{326/930}{506/930} = 0\cdot644.$

(b) $P(TS|SM) = \dfrac{P(TS \cap SM)}{P(SM)} = \dfrac{104/930}{424/930} = 0\cdot245.$

(c) $P(SM|TS) = \dfrac{P(SM \cap TS)}{P(TS)} = \dfrac{104/930}{430/930} = 0\cdot242.$

It is important to notice that $P(TS|SM)$ is not the same as $P(SM|TS)$. The former is the probability that, given a short mother, then the son is tall. The latter is the probability that given a tall son, the mother is short.

Example 7 Find the probability of drawing 2 spades when drawing 2 cards from a well-shuffled pack.

Here we must know how the 2 cards are to be drawn; the question alone does not give us sufficient information for us to find an answer. We must know whether the cards are drawn *with replacement* or *without replacement*.
(a) If we draw a card, then replace it in the pack (*with replacement*), and then draw again, we have

$$P(S_1 \text{ and } S_2) = P(S_1).P(S_2),$$

since the two events of drawing a spade are independent. That is,

$$P(S_1 \text{ and } S_2) = \tfrac{13}{52} \cdot \tfrac{13}{52} = \tfrac{1}{16}.$$

(b) If we draw a card, *do not* replace it in the pack, and then draw again (*without replacement*), the two events of obtaining a spade are now dependent, for the second draw probability depends on whether or not we have drawn a spade on the first draw.

$$P(\text{spade on first draw}) = P(S_1) = \tfrac{13}{52} = \tfrac{1}{4}.$$

The pack is now down to 51 cards. We need

$$P(S_1 \text{ and } S_2) = P(S_1).P(S_2|S_1).$$

Given that a spade was drawn the first time, there are now 12 spades in the 51 cards and we have

$$P(S_1 \text{ and } S_2) = \tfrac{1}{4}.\tfrac{12}{51} = \tfrac{1}{17}.$$

The same method and result would apply if the 2 cards were drawn simultaneously (as a pair) from the pack.

As an alternative method we could use

$$P(S_1 \text{ and } S_2) = \binom{13}{2} \Big/ \binom{52}{2} = \frac{1}{17}.$$

Example 8   In a certain strain of wallflower, the probability that a seed produces a plant with yellow flowers is $\tfrac{1}{4}$. Find the number of seeds that should be sown in order that the probability of obtaining at least one plant with yellow flowers will be greater than 0·99.

Let the number of seeds be n. Probability of yellow flowers is $\tfrac{1}{4}$. Probability of not yellow flowers is $\tfrac{3}{4}$.

P(at least one plant with yellow flowers) = $1 - $ P(none with yellow flowers)

$$= 1 - \left(\frac{3}{4}\right)^n > 0.99$$

$$\Rightarrow 0.01 > \left(\frac{3}{4}\right)^n$$

$$\Rightarrow \left(\frac{4}{3}\right)^n > 100$$

$$\Rightarrow n(\lg 4 - \lg 3) > \lg 100 = 2$$

$$\Rightarrow n > \frac{2}{\lg 4 - \lg 3} = 16.01$$

i.e. 17 seeds must be sown.

Exercise 1.2

1   A box contains 4 red buttons and 4 white buttons. Find the probability that, when 2 buttons are chosen at random and without replacement, 1 will be red and 1 will be white.

2   A committee of 3 is chosen at random from a group of 20 people consisting of 12 men and 8 women. Find the probability that
   (a) exactly 2 men are chosen,
   (b) exactly 2 women are chosen.

3   For the two events E and F, $P(E) = \tfrac{1}{2}$, $P(F) = \tfrac{1}{3}$ and $P(E \cap F) = \tfrac{1}{5}$. Find
   (a) $P(E|F)$, (b) $P(F|E)$, (c) $P(E \cup F)$, (d) $P(E'|F')$.

4   The independent probabilities that John and Bill hit a target at rifle practice are $\tfrac{1}{3}$ and $\tfrac{1}{4}$, respectively.

(a) Given that each of them fires twice, find the probability that the target will be hit at least once.

(b) Given that John can fire only once, find the least number of times that Bill must fire so that there is a probability of at least 0·95 that the target will be hit.

(c) Given that John and Bill each fire once, and the target is hit only once, find the probability that it will be John who hits the target.

1.3 Tree diagrams and Bayes' theorem

The solution of some probability questions can be made easier by the use of a *tree diagram* showing all the possible outcomes. For this, we represent by the 'branches' of a 'tree' all the possible outcomes of the first event, attaching to each branch the probability of that particular outcome occurring. Then, from the ends of each of these branches, we draw branches representing all the possible outcomes of the second event, with their corresponding probabilities of occurrence attached. In the same way we continue for the total number of events with which we are concerned. If we then follow one (or more) particular 'branch line(s)', we can find the probability of a particular combination of outcomes in the events.

For example, suppose we have two boxes A and B. Box A contains 3 red (*R*) and 4 white (*W*) balls. Box B contains 5 red and 3 white balls. We choose a box at random and then choose a ball at random from that box. The probability tree diagram is shown in Fig. 1.3.

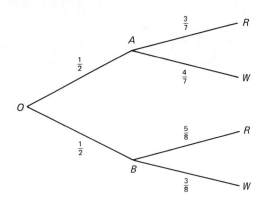

Fig. 1.3

$$P(A) = P(B) = \tfrac{1}{2}.$$

In box A, $P(R) = \tfrac{3}{7}$, $P(W) = \tfrac{4}{7}$.
In box B, $P(R) = \tfrac{5}{8}$, $P(W) = \tfrac{3}{8}$.

We then follow along any route from O to the tip of a branch and we obtain the probability by multiplying together the probabilities on the branches. Hence,

$$P(A \cap R) = \tfrac{1}{2} \times \tfrac{3}{7} = \tfrac{3}{14}.$$

It can be seen that, if we have a total of k events, and the numbers of possible outcomes are, respectively, $n_1, n_2, \ldots, n_k$ for the 1st, 2nd, $\ldots$, kth events, then the total number of possible outcomes for the k events is $n_1 \times n_2 \times n_3 \times \ldots \times n_k$. Hence, the number of branches in a tree diagram obviously increases very rapidly as the number of events increases.

Example 9 When a person needs a minicab, he hires one from one of three firms A, B, or C. Of his hirings, 60% are from firm A, 30% from B and 10% from C. From firm A, 9% of the cabs arrive late; from B, 20% arrive late; and from C, 6% arrive late. Find
(a) the probability that a cab chosen at random from those he hires will be from firm C and will not be late,
(b) the probability that a cab hired by the person will be late.

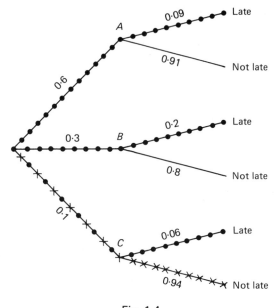

Fig. 1.4

Using the tree diagram in Fig. 1.4, we have
(a) the *crossed* branch line
$\Rightarrow$ P($C \cap$ not late) = 0·1 × 0·94
$\qquad\qquad\qquad\quad$ = 0·094,
(b) the sum of the 3 *dotted* 'branch lines'
$\Rightarrow$ P(late) = 0·6 × 0·09 + 0·3 × 0·2 + 0·1 × 0·06
$\qquad\qquad$ = 0·12.

Let us look now at a problem where the words seem a hopeless tangle but a tree diagram (Fig. 1.5) makes the solution quite simple.

Example 10   A headmaster knows that for the science sixth form at his school, the odds are 1 to 2 that a pupil will take chemistry (*C*). If a pupil does take chemistry, the odds are 3 to 1 that he or she will take physics (*P*), and if a pupil does not take chemistry, the odds are 7 to 1 that he or she will take physics. If a pupil takes both chemistry and physics, the odds are 5 to 1 that he or she also takes mathematics (*M*); if a pupil takes chemistry but not physics, the odds are 1 to 4 that he or she also takes mathematics. For a pupil who takes neither chemistry nor physics, the odds are 3 to 1 that he or she takes mathematics; for a pupil taking physics but not chemistry, the odds are 9 to 1 that he or she takes mathematics. Find the probability that a pupil chosen at random

(a) from this science sixth form takes mathematics,

(b) from this science sixth form does not take any of the subjects mathematics, chemistry or physics,

(c) from those who take mathematics, also takes chemistry,

(d) from those who take both mathematics and physics, also takes chemistry.

Fig. 1.5 shows the tree diagram for this problem.

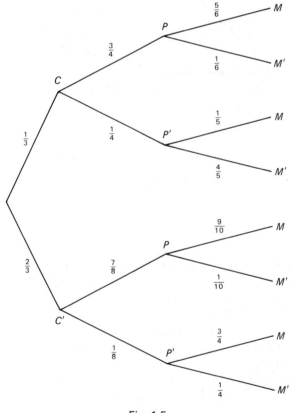

Fig. 1.5

(a) $P(M) = \frac{1}{3} \times \frac{3}{4} \times \frac{5}{6} + \frac{1}{3} \times \frac{1}{4} \times \frac{1}{5} + \frac{2}{3} \times \frac{7}{8} \times \frac{9}{10} + \frac{2}{3} \times \frac{1}{8} \times \frac{3}{4} = \frac{13}{16}.$

(b) P(none of the three subjects) $= P(C' \cap P' \cap M') = \frac{2}{3} \times \frac{1}{8} \times \frac{1}{4} = \frac{1}{48}.$

(c) $P(C|M) = \dfrac{P(C \cap M)}{P(M)} = \dfrac{\frac{1}{3}(\frac{3}{4} \times \frac{5}{6} + \frac{1}{4} \times \frac{1}{5})}{\frac{13}{16}} = \dfrac{18}{65}.$

(d) $P(C|P \cap M) = \dfrac{P(C \cap P \cap M)}{P(P \cap M)} = \dfrac{\frac{1}{3} \times \frac{3}{4} \times \frac{5}{6}}{\frac{1}{3} \times \frac{3}{4} \times \frac{5}{6} + \frac{2}{3} \times \frac{7}{8} \times \frac{9}{10}} = \dfrac{25}{88}.$

Example 11 Let us look again at Example 9 of p. 11, and ask the question: 'If a minicab is called and it arrives late, what is the probability that it came from firm *B*'?

Now $P(B|\text{late}) = \dfrac{P(B \cap \text{late})}{P(\text{late})} = \dfrac{0 \cdot 3 \times 0 \cdot 2}{0 \cdot 12} = 0 \cdot 5.$

[We asked, and answered, the same type of question in Example 10(c) and (d).]

How is the solution built up?

$$P(B|\text{late}) = \frac{P(B \cap \text{late})}{P(\text{late})} = \frac{P(B).P(\text{late}|B)}{P(\text{late})}$$

$$= \frac{P(B).P(\text{late}|B)}{P(A).P(\text{late}|A) + P(B).P(\text{late}|B) + P(C).P(\text{late}|C)}$$

$(= 0 \cdot 5$ in our problem).

We can now state *Bayes' theorem*, which expresses this result in symbolic form. Given that $B_1, B_2, \ldots, B_n$ are a mutually exclusive and exhaustive set of outcomes of a random process, and E is a chance event (where $P(E) \neq 0$) caused by, or preceded by, one of the events $B_1, B_2, \ldots, B_n$, then

$$P(B_k|E) = \frac{P(B_k).P(E|B_k)}{\displaystyle\sum_{r=1}^{n} P(B_r).P(E|B_r)}$$

for $k = 1, 2, \ldots, n$.

Proof (of Bayes' theorem) From the definition of conditional probability, we have

$$P(B_k|E) = \frac{P(B_k \cap E)}{P(E)} = \frac{P(B_k).P(E|B_k)}{P(E)}.$$

Since event E is caused by, or preceded by, one of the events B_k, $k = 1, 2, \ldots, n$, then

$$P(E) = P(E \cap B_1) + P(E \cap B_2) + \cdots + P(E \cap B_n)$$

$$= \sum_{r=1}^{n} P(E \cap B_r)$$

$$= \sum_{r=1}^{n} P(B_r) . P(E|B_r)$$

$$\Rightarrow P(B_k|E) = \frac{P(B_k) . P(E|B_k)}{\sum_{r=1}^{n} P(B_r) . P(E|B_r)}.$$

Example 12 In a large company, 15% of the employees are graduates (G), and, of these, 80% work in administrative posts (A). Of the non-graduate (NG) employees of the company, 10% work in administrative posts. Find the probability that an employee of this company selected at random from those working in administrative posts will be a graduate.

We have

$$P(G) = 0.15, \ P(NG) = 0.85, \ P(A|NG) = 0.10, \ P(A|G) = 0.80,$$
$$P(G) . P(A|G) = 0.15 \times 0.80, \text{ and } P(NG) . P(A|NG) = 0.85 \times 0.10.$$

Bayes' theorem gives

$$P(G|A) = \frac{P(G) . P(A|G)}{P(G) . P(A|G) + P(NG) . P(A|NG)}$$

$$= \frac{0.15 \times 0.80}{0.15 \times 0.80 + 0.85 \times 0.10} = 0.585.$$

Exercise 1.3

1 We have two boxes A and B, where A contains 2 red and 3 white balls, B contains 5 red and 4 white balls. We toss a coin, and, if we get a head, we take a ball at random from box A, but if we get a tail we take a ball at random from box B. We toss the coin once. Use a tree diagram to find the probability that we will take a red ball.

2 We have two boxes A and B, where A contains 5 tickets numbered from 1 to 5 and B contains 7 tickets numbered from 1 to 7. We choose one of the two boxes at random and then pick a ticket from it at random. Use a tree diagram or Bayes' theorem to find the probability that the ticket comes from box B, given that its number is odd.

3 Steel girders are manufactured by three factories A, B and C. Each month, factory A makes twice as many as factory B, and factories B and C make the same number of girders. Of the girders made by factory A and of those made by B, 2% are defective; of those made by C, 4% are defective. One month's production of girders of the three factories is put into a warehouse. Given that one girder is chosen at random from the warehouse,
(a) find the probability that this item will be defective,
(b) given that the girder is defective, find the probability that it comes from factory A.

4 A box contains 6 batteries, of which 2 are known to be flat. The batteries are tested one after the other until the 2 flat batteries are found. Find the probability that the 2 flat batteries will be found when just 2 batteries have been tested. Find also the probability that the 2 flat batteries will be found only when just 3 batteries have been tested.

1.4 Markov chains

Consider the problem of a shopper who is buying margarine (Ma) or butter (Bu) (but not both). Suppose that it has been found that, when she buys margarine on a given shopping outing, there is a probability of 0·8 that she will buy margarine the next time she purchases, and a probability of 0·2 that she buys butter instead. Also, if she buys butter on the given outing, the probability that she buys butter the next time is 0·6 and the probability is 0·4 that she buys margarine. Suppose further that, on the first purchase being considered, there is an equal chance that she will buy butter or margarine. What is the probability that she will buy butter on (a) the third, (b) the ninth purchase? We draw the tree diagram, Fig. 1.6. Then

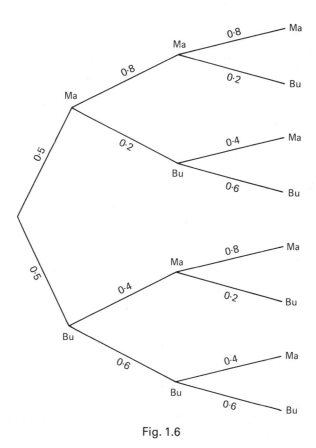

Fig. 1.6

P(Bu on second purchase) $\equiv$ P(Bu_2) $= 0\cdot5 \times 0\cdot2 + 0\cdot5 \times 0\cdot6 = 0\cdot4$
$\Rightarrow$ P(Ma_2) $= 1 - 0\cdot4 = 0\cdot6$ (or $0\cdot5 \times 0\cdot8 + 0\cdot5 \times 0\cdot4$).

Also

P(Bu_3) $= 0\cdot5 \times 0\cdot8 \times 0\cdot2 + 0\cdot5 \times 0\cdot2 \times 0\cdot6 + 0\cdot5 \times 0\cdot4 \times 0\cdot2 + 0\cdot5 \times 0\cdot6 \times 0\cdot6$
       $= 0\cdot36$

$\Rightarrow$ P(Ma_3) $= 0\cdot64$.

We could find probabilities for the fourth purchase in the same way, but the tree diagram becomes rather large and cumbersome, and for the ninth purchase it would be quite unmanageable. Let us look at the previous results, using the notation P(Bu_k), P(Ma_k) for the probabilities of purchasing butter and margarine, respectively, on the kth purchase.

$$(P(Bu_2), P(Ma_2)) = (0\cdot5(0\cdot6 + 0\cdot2), 0\cdot5(0\cdot4 + 0\cdot8))$$
$$= (0\cdot5, 0\cdot5)\begin{pmatrix} 0\cdot6 & 0\cdot4 \\ 0\cdot2 & 0\cdot8 \end{pmatrix}$$
$$= (P(Bu_1), P(Ma_1))\begin{pmatrix} 0\cdot6 & 0\cdot4 \\ 0\cdot2 & 0\cdot8 \end{pmatrix}.$$

If we denote the *probability row vectors* (P(Bu_k), P(Ma_k)), for $k = 1, 2, \ldots$, by $\mathbf{p}_1, \mathbf{p}_2, \mathbf{p}_3, \ldots$, we have $\mathbf{p}_2 = \mathbf{p}_1 \mathbf{M}$, where

$$\mathbf{M} = \begin{pmatrix} 0\cdot6 & 0\cdot4 \\ 0\cdot2 & 0\cdot8 \end{pmatrix}.$$

Here the matrix $\mathbf{M}$ is called the *transition matrix*, and it is the fixed matrix of probabilities which takes us from one state (purchasing occasion in our example) to the next state (next purchasing occasion).
Similarly,

$$\mathbf{p}_3 = (P(Bu_3), P(Ma_3)) = (0\cdot5(0\cdot6 \times 0\cdot6 + 0\cdot4 \times 0\cdot2 + 0\cdot2 \times 0\cdot6 + 0\cdot8 \times 0\cdot2),$$
$$0\cdot5(0\cdot6 \times 0\cdot4 + 0\cdot4 \times 0\cdot8 + 0\cdot2 \times 0\cdot4 + 0\cdot8 \times 0\cdot8))$$
$$= ([0\cdot5(0\cdot6 + 0\cdot2)0\cdot6 + 0\cdot5(0\cdot4 + 0\cdot8)0\cdot2],$$
$$[0\cdot5(0\cdot6 + 0\cdot2)0\cdot4 + 0\cdot5(0\cdot4 + 0\cdot8)0\cdot8])$$
$$= (0\cdot5(0\cdot6 + 0\cdot2), 0\cdot5(0\cdot4 + 0\cdot8))\begin{pmatrix} 0\cdot6 & 0\cdot4 \\ 0\cdot2 & 0\cdot8 \end{pmatrix}$$
$$= \mathbf{p}_2 \mathbf{M} = \mathbf{p}_1 \mathbf{M}^2.$$

It seems probable that

$$\mathbf{p}_4 = \mathbf{p}_3 \mathbf{M} = \mathbf{p}_2 \mathbf{M}^2 = \mathbf{p}_1 \mathbf{M}^3, \quad \mathbf{p}_5 = \mathbf{p}_1 \mathbf{M}^4, \text{ etc.},$$

and in fact these can all be shown by use of the tree diagram and by multiplying the probability vectors by $\mathbf{M}$. The general result $\mathbf{p}_k = \mathbf{p}_1 \mathbf{M}^{k-1}$, where k is a positive integer, may be shown by induction.

Thus, for P(Bu_9), instead of drawing a very large tree diagram, we could get our result by post-multiplying $\mathbf{p}_1$ by $\mathbf{M}^8$.

The calculations for the vectors $\mathbf{p}_1$, $\mathbf{p}_2$, $\mathbf{p}_3$, $\mathbf{p}_4$, $\mathbf{p}_5$, $\mathbf{p}_6$, $\mathbf{p}_7$, $\mathbf{p}_8$, $\mathbf{p}_9$, give $(0{\cdot}5, 0{\cdot}5)$, $(0{\cdot}4, 0{\cdot}6)$, $(0{\cdot}36, 0{\cdot}64)$, $(0{\cdot}344, 0{\cdot}656)$, $(0{\cdot}338, 0{\cdot}662)$, $(0{\cdot}335, 0{\cdot}665)$, $(0{\cdot}334, 0{\cdot}666)$, $(0{\cdot}3336, 0{\cdot}6664)$, $(0{\cdot}333\,44, 0{\cdot}666\,56)$, respectively, and it appears that $\mathbf{p}_k$ may be tending to a limit vector of $(\frac{1}{3}, \frac{2}{3})$. You will notice that, because the elements of the row vectors are probabilities, the sum of the elements must add up to 1, certainty. If $\mathbf{p}_{k+1} = \mathbf{p}_k \mathbf{M} = \mathbf{p}_k$ for some value of k, then we say that $\mathbf{p}_k$ is the equilibrium state $\mathbf{p}$, and this will be the probability vector for all further events, since $\mathbf{p}_{k+2} = \mathbf{p}_{k+1}\mathbf{M} = \mathbf{p}_k\mathbf{M} = \mathbf{p}_k = \mathbf{p}$.

This would imply that the probability of buying butter and the probability of buying margarine would each be constant for all events from the kth onwards.

In a problem of this kind, where the probability of the rth event depends only on the result of the $(r-1)$th event, and where the transition matrix is the same for each successive pair of events, we are dealing with a *Markov chain*, and using a *Markov process*. The equilibrium state (or limiting vector), $\mathbf{p}$, can be found from the equation $\mathbf{p}\mathbf{M} = \mathbf{p}$, provided that we know $\mathbf{M}$, and it is, of course, independent of the initial probability vector $\mathbf{p}_1$. Our example has involved row vectors with two elements and $\mathbf{M}$, a 2×2 matrix, but a Markov process is not, of course, restricted to these. It can be used for $\mathbf{M}$, an $n \times n$ matrix, and row vectors of n elements, where n is any positive integer.

Example 13   For the transition matrix $\begin{pmatrix} \frac{1}{5} & \frac{4}{5} \\ \frac{3}{4} & \frac{1}{4} \end{pmatrix}$ of a Markov process, find the limit to which the probability vector will tend.

In the equilibrium state

$$(p,q)\begin{pmatrix} \frac{1}{5} & \frac{4}{5} \\ \frac{3}{4} & \frac{1}{4} \end{pmatrix} = (p,q), \quad \text{where } p + q = 1,$$

$$\Rightarrow \left. \begin{cases} \frac{1}{5}p + \frac{3}{4}q = p \\ \frac{4}{5}p + \frac{1}{4}q = q \\ p + q = 1 \end{cases} \right\} \Rightarrow p = \tfrac{15}{31}, \quad q = \tfrac{16}{31}.$$

Here we have three equations in two unknowns but the equations are *consistent* — that is, the solutions for p and q satisfy all three equations. The limit probability vector is $(\frac{15}{31}, \frac{16}{31})$.

Example 14   If a man leaves home too late to catch his bus to work on any day, the probability that he is late the following day is $\frac{1}{3}$, whereas if he leaves in time to catch it on any day, then the probability that he is late on the following day is $\frac{3}{5}$. The man catches his bus on Tuesday and leaves for work each day.
(a) Write down the transition matrix.
(b) Calculate the probability that he catches his bus on the following Friday.

(c) Show that, over a long period, the probability that he will catch his bus to work is $\frac{10}{19}$.

(a) The transition matrix is $\begin{pmatrix} \frac{2}{5} & \frac{3}{5} \\ \frac{2}{3} & \frac{1}{3} \end{pmatrix}$.

(b) Wednesday probability vector is

$$(P(\text{catches}),\ P(\text{late})) = (\tfrac{2}{5}, \tfrac{3}{5}),$$

$$\text{Friday probability vector} = (\tfrac{2}{5}, \tfrac{3}{5})\begin{pmatrix} \frac{2}{5} & \frac{3}{5} \\ \frac{2}{3} & \frac{1}{3} \end{pmatrix}^2$$

$$= (\tfrac{2}{5}, \tfrac{3}{5})\begin{pmatrix} \frac{14}{25} & \frac{11}{25} \\ \frac{22}{45} & \frac{23}{45} \end{pmatrix} = (\tfrac{194}{375}, \tfrac{181}{375}),$$

$\Rightarrow$ P(catches it on Friday) $= \frac{194}{375}$.

(c) In the equilibrium state

$$(p,q)\begin{pmatrix} \frac{2}{5} & \frac{3}{5} \\ \frac{2}{3} & \frac{1}{3} \end{pmatrix} = (p,q), \text{ and } p + q = 1.$$

$\frac{2}{5}p + \frac{2}{3}q = p,$

$\Rightarrow p + q = 1,$ $\Rightarrow p = \frac{10}{19}$ in the equilibrium state.

Hence, probability (over a long period) that he catches his bus is $\frac{10}{19}$.

Exercise 1.4

1 If Joan is late for work, she makes a greater effort to arrive on time the following work day. If she arrives on time, she is liable to be less careful the next day. Consequently, if she is late one day, the probability that she will be on time the next day is $\frac{3}{4}$. If she is on time one day, the probability that she will be late the next day is $\frac{1}{2}$. Given that she is on time on Monday, calculate the probability that in the same week she will be on time (a) on the Thursday, (b) on the Friday.

Show that, in the long run, she will be on time $1\frac{1}{2}$ times as often as she is late.

2 If I stay home one evening, the probability that I do not stay home the following evening is 0.7, but if I do not stay home one evening, the probability that I do not stay home the next evening is 0.6. Write down the transition matrix. Find the probability that, over a long period, I will stay home on any evening.

Miscellaneous Exercise 1

1 When three marksmen, A, B and C, take part in a shooting contest their independent chances of hitting the target are $\frac{3}{5}, \frac{1}{3}$ and $\frac{1}{4}$, respectively. Calculate the probability that one, and only one, bullet will hit the target when all three marksmen fire at it simultaneously.

2 The independent probabilities that 3 light bulbs in a car will need replacing within a year are $\frac{1}{10}, \frac{1}{12}$ and $\frac{1}{15}$. Calculate the probability that, within a year, (a) none, (b) at least 1, (c) 1 and only 1 of the 3 light bulbs will need replacing.

3 Three civil servants, Smith, Jones and Brown, retire on the same day. If at least 2

of them are still alive 5 years later, they agree that the survivors will meet. Find, to three decimal places, the probability that they will meet as agreed, given that the independent probabilities of their each living 5 years after retirement are $\frac{5}{8}$, $\frac{7}{10}$, $\frac{6}{7}$, respectively.

4 Let A and B be events with $P(A \cup B) = \frac{7}{8}$, $P(A \cap B) = \frac{1}{4}$ and $P(A') = \frac{5}{8}$. Find $P(A)$, $P(B')$ and $P(A \cap B')$.

5 Three balls are taken at random without replacement from a bag containing 5 yellow, 4 green and 3 red balls. Find the probability that
(a) all 3 are of the same colour,
(b) all 3 are of different colours,
(c) 2 are of the same colour and the third is of a different colour.

6 A box A contains a red, b green and c pink cards. A similar box B contains p red, q green and r pink cards. A boy tosses a coin and, if it shows 'heads', he chooses 2 cards at random from box A but if it shows 'tails', he chooses 2 cards at random from box B. If there are 50 cards in each box and drawing is without replacement, show that the probability that both cards drawn are of the same colour is

$$\frac{1}{4900}(a^2 + b^2 + c^2 + p^2 + q^2 + r^2) - \frac{1}{49}.$$

7 It is known that 0·03% of the population suffer from a particular disease. A test to discover the disease shows a positive reaction for 90% of people suffering from the disease, and also for 1·5% of people not suffering from it. A randomly selected person shows a positive reaction to the test. Find, to three decimal places, the probability that that person does have the disease.

8 A and B are two events. Show that $P(A)$ lies between $P(A|B)$ and $P(A|B')$.

9 A battery contains only two breeds of hens, X and Y; 75% of the egg production is from hens of breed X. Of the eggs laid by the X hens, 25% are size 1, 55% are size 2 and the remainder size 3. For the Y hens, the corresponding proportions are 35%, 40% and 25%. Egg colour (brown or white) is independent of size in each breed; 40% of X eggs and 30% of Y eggs are brown. Find
(a) the probability that an egg laid by a Y hen is size 1 and brown,
(b) the probability that an egg is size 1 and white,
(c) the probability that a white egg is size 1,
(d) which size grade contains the smallest proportion of white eggs.

10 A survey of 500 graduates studying one or more courses in mathematics, physics and chemistry gave the following numbers of students attending classes in the indicated subjects:

mathematics	256	both mathematics and physics	80
physics	262	both physics and chemistry	165
chemistry	340	both mathematics and chemistry	158

Find the probability that a student selected at random from the group takes all three subjects.

11 If the sun shines one day, the probability that it shines the next day is $\frac{7}{10}$, but if it does not shine, the probability that it shines the next day is $\frac{2}{5}$. The sun does not shine on Monday. Calculate the probability that it will shine on Wednesday of the same week.

12 The probability of a darts team winning a match is 0·5 and of drawing is 0·3, if the previous match was won. If the previous match was drawn, the probability of winning is 0·3 and of drawing is 0·4. If the previous match was lost, the probability of winning is 0·1 and of drawing is 0·3. Find the transition matrix, and hence find

the probabilities of the team winning, of drawing and of losing any particular darts match in the distant future, if the probabilities remain the same.

13 Given that events A and B are independent and that $P(A) = \frac{1}{4}$ and $P(A \cap B) = \frac{1}{20}$, find $P(B)$, $P(B|A)$, and $P(A \cup B)$.

14 Given that $P(A) = \frac{2}{5}$, $P(B|A) = \frac{1}{8}$, $P(B|A') = \frac{1}{4}$, determine
(a) $P(B \cap A)$, (b) $P(B \cap A')$.

15 A bag contains 18 sweets, 3 of which are yellow and 15 of which are green. Sweets are drawn at random from this bag, one at a time and without replacement, until the first yellow sweet appears. Calculate the probability that this occurs on the fifth drawing.

16 Each of three identical boxes, X, Y and Z, has two drawers. Box X does not contain any coins. Box Y contains one coin only. Box Z contains one coin in each drawer. A box is chosen at random and a drawer is opened and found to be empty. Find the probability that a coin will be found
(a) if the other drawer in the same box is opened,
(b) if one of the other two boxes is chosen at random and a drawer is opened.

17 In a tasting trial, two pieces of cheddar cheese — one processed cheese, the other farmhouse cheese — are tasted and the taster is asked to identify the farmhouse cheese. Assuming that the taster cannot distinguish between the two types of cheese,
(a) find the probability that the taster has at least 4 successes in 5 trials;
(b) find the smallest value for n that will ensure that, in n trials, there is a probability of at least 0·95 of the taster obtaining at least one success;
(c) find the smallest value for n that will ensure that, in n trials, there is a probability of at most 0·5 of the taster obtaining fewer than 2 successes.

18 Three dice are to be thrown and the total score, S, is to be recorded. Find the probability that
(a) S will be either 8 or 9,
(b) $5 \leqslant S \leqslant 11$,
(c) S will be odd.
Find the probability that only one '6' will be thrown.

2 Probability distributions

2.1 Random variables

In Chapter 1 we saw that, for some experiments, the sample space (that is, the set of all possible outcomes) is a set of numerical values, whereas in others the outcomes are non-numerical. For example, the experiment of throwing a fair die and noting the number obtained has numerical outcomes, whereas the experiment of tossing a coin once has just two outcomes, 'head' or 'tail', forming the sample space. However, even in this latter example we could assign numbers 1 and 0 to 'head' and 'tail', respectively and so make each of the outcomes a numerical quantity.

In probability work we are often interested in real numbers which either represent, or are assigned to, the outcomes of chance experiments; thus, every element (outcome) of the sample space S is associated with a unique numerical value x. This means that a function X is defined over all the points of the sample space, and x is the value of the function X at that particular element of S. Such a function X is called a *random variable*, and X may be discrete (if the number of possible outcomes is finite or countably infinite) or continuous (if X may assume all values in some interval $a < x < b$, where a, b may be infinite).

2.2 Discrete probability distributions

We have discussed in the previous chapter methods of finding the probability P of a certain outcome occurring. If we denote by $p(x)$ the probability that the discrete random variable X takes the value x, then $p(x)$, where $P(X = x) \equiv p(x)$, is called the *probability function* of X. The points given by $(x_1, p(x_1))$, $(x_2, p(x_2))$, $\ldots$, for all the elements of the sample space (say, n elements), can be plotted on a diagram (Fig. 2.1). This provides a visual illustration of the *probability distribution*. Since the sum of all the possible outcomes is 1 (certainty), we have

$$\sum_{r=1}^{n} p(x_r) = 1.$$

We also define the *distribution function* $F(x)$ by the equation

$$F(x_r) = P(X \leqslant x_r) = \sum_{i=1}^{i=r} p(x_i).$$

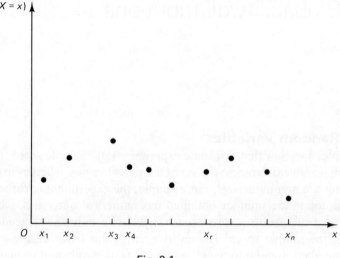

Fig. 2.1

The function $F(x)$ is the *cumulative probability function* of X from the lowest value of X, x_1, up to and including the value x_r.

Example 1   The probability function of a discrete random variable X is given by

$$p(x) = \frac{k}{2^x}, \quad x = 1, 2, \ldots.$$

(a) Find the value of k.
(b) Find $P(X \leqslant 3)$.

(a) $\Sigma p(x) = 1$

$$\Rightarrow \sum_{x=1}^{\infty} \frac{k}{2^x} = 1 = \frac{k \cdot \frac{1}{2}}{(1 - \frac{1}{2})} = k;$$

since this is an infinite geometric progression with $a = r = \frac{1}{2}$ in the usual notation,

$$\Rightarrow k = 1.$$

(b) $P(X \leqslant 3) = p(1) + p(2) + p(3)$
$$= \frac{1}{2} + \frac{1}{2^2} + \frac{1}{2^3} = \frac{7}{8}.$$

The *expectation* or *expected mean value*, $E(X)$, of a discrete random variable X is defined as

$$E(X) = \Sigma x p(x)$$

summed over all the possible values of X. That is, it is the sum of the products of all the possible values of the random variable and their respective probabilities. Sometimes we use the symbol μ (Greek mu) for $E(X)$.

Example 2   A collector for charity asks you to put a coin in his tin. In your pocket are three 1p, two 2p, four 5p and one 10p pieces. If you put your hand into your pocket and pull out a single coin at random to put in his tin, find the expected amount that you will thus give.

$$P(X = 1) = \tfrac{3}{10}, \; P(X = 2) = \tfrac{1}{5}, \; P(X = 5) = \tfrac{2}{5}, \; P(X = 10) = \tfrac{1}{10}.$$

Hence,

$$E(X) = (1 \times \tfrac{3}{10} + 2 \times \tfrac{1}{5} + 5 \times \tfrac{2}{5} + 10 \times \tfrac{1}{10}) \text{ pence} = 3\tfrac{7}{10} \text{ pence}.$$

If we considered a very large number of repeated trials of an experiment, then the average value of the random variable X for these trials would be very close to the expected mean. The expected mean, as we see above, may be an impossible value for any given trial, since, in the case of Example 2, on any given trial the coin donated will be either a 1p, 2p, 5p or 10p coin. $E(X)$ is the value found when we calculate the mean of all the possible values of X in this experiment; it is the mean of the probability distribution of X.

We can show that, if X is a discrete random variable and a and b are constants, then

$$E(aX + b) = aE(X) + b.$$

Proof   Whenever X takes the value x, $aX + b$ takes the value $ax + b$,

$$\Rightarrow P(aX + b = ax + b) = P(X = x) = p(x),$$

since a, b are constants.
Thus

$$\begin{aligned}
E(aX + b) &= \Sigma(ax + b).p(ax + b) \\
&= \Sigma(ax + b).p(x) \\
&= a\Sigma xp(x) + b\Sigma p(x) \\
&= aE(X) + b, \text{ because } \Sigma p(x) = 1.
\end{aligned}$$

The mean of the sum and difference of two discrete random variables X and Y

It can be proved that, if X and Y are two discrete random variables, then

$$E(X + Y) = E(X) + E(Y),$$
$$E(X - Y) = E(X) - E(Y).$$

The proofs of these results are beyond the scope of this text, but we illustrate these results by an example.

Example 3 Suppose that an experiment consists of tossing a fair die and a fair coin, X being the outcome on the die and Y the outcome on the coin. For the outcome Y, we denote a head by 1 and a tail by 0. The sample spaces are

for X: 1, 2, 3, 4, 5, 6, each with probability $\frac{1}{6}$;

for Y: 0, 1, each with probability $\frac{1}{2}$;

for (X, Y): (1,0), (2,0), (3,0), (4,0), (5,0), (6,0), (1,1), (2,1), (3,1), (4,1), (5,1), (6,1), each with probability $\frac{1}{12}$.

$$E(X + Y) = \tfrac{1}{12}(1 + 2 + 3 + 4 + 5 + 6 + 2 + 3 + 4 + 5 + 6 + 7) = \tfrac{48}{12} = 4.$$
$$E(X) = \tfrac{1}{6}(1 + 2 + 3 + 4 + 5 + 6) = \tfrac{7}{2}.$$
$$E(Y) = \tfrac{1}{2}(0 + 1) = \tfrac{1}{2}.$$

Hence, in this case,

$$E(X + Y) = E(X) + E(Y).$$

Also

$$E(X - Y) = \tfrac{1}{12}(1 + 2 + 3 + 4 + 5 + 6 + 0 + 1 + 2 + 3 + 4 + 5)$$
$$= \tfrac{36}{12} = 3 = E(X) - E(Y).$$

The expected mean is not the only quantity of interest in a probability distribution; we are interested also in how the values of the random variable X are spread about the mean. Two distributions could have the same expected mean, yet in one the X-values might be closely grouped around the mean, whereas in the other the distribution might be widely spread.

Consider the two distributions

(i) $P(X = x) = p(x) = \frac{1}{3}$ for $x = 5, 50, 95$,

(ii) $P(X = x) = p(x) = \frac{1}{3}$ for $x = 45, 50, 55$.

For (i),

$$E(X) = \tfrac{1}{3}(5 + 50 + 95) = 50.$$

For (ii),

$$E(X) = \tfrac{1}{3}(45 + 50 + 55) = 50.$$

So the expected means are equal but we can see from Fig. 2.2 that the distributions are quite different in the way that the values of X are spread about the mean value 50.

There are various measures of *spread* or *dispersion* which can be used, the one most commonly used being the *variance*. We define the variance of X, written $\mathrm{Var}(X)$, as

$$\mathrm{Var}(X) = E[X - E(X)]^2,$$

and this is often denoted by the symbol σ^2. The positive square root of $\mathrm{Var}(X)$ is called the *standard deviation* of X (often written as S.D. $= \sigma$). The

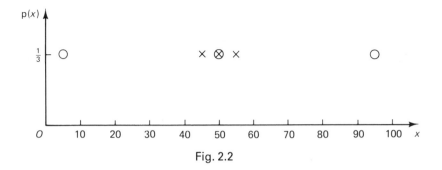

Fig. 2.2

standard deviation is measured in the same units as those in which X is measured.

The evaluation of $\text{Var}(X)$ can be simplified by using the result

$$\text{Var}(X) = E(X^2) - \mu^2.$$

Proof

$$
\begin{aligned}
\text{Var}(X) &= E[X - \mu]^2 = E[X^2 - 2\mu X + \mu^2] \\
&= E(X^2) - 2\mu E(X) + \mu^2, \text{ since } \mu \text{ is a constant.} \\
&= E(X^2) - 2\mu^2 + \mu^2, \text{ since } E(X) = \mu, \\
&= E(X^2) - \mu^2, \\
&= \Sigma x^2 p(x) - \mu^2, \text{ the summation being taken over all the values of } X.
\end{aligned}
$$

Example 4   We return to Example 2, the coins in the pocket problem. We found that $\mu = 3\frac{7}{10}$ pence. We now calculate $\text{Var}(X)$.

$$
\begin{aligned}
\text{Var}(X) &= [\Sigma x^2 p(x) - \mu^2] \text{ (pence)}^2 \\
&= [1^2 \times \tfrac{3}{10} + 2^2 \times \tfrac{1}{5} + 5^2 \times \tfrac{2}{5} + 10^2 \times \tfrac{1}{10} - (\tfrac{37}{10})^2] \text{ (pence)}^2 \\
&= 7\cdot41 \text{ (pence)}^2,
\end{aligned}
$$

and S.D. $\approx 2\cdot72$ pence.

Had we calculated this using the definition, we would have had

$$
\begin{aligned}
\text{Var}(X) &= [(1 - \tfrac{37}{10})^2 \times \tfrac{3}{10} + (2 - \tfrac{37}{10})^2 \times \tfrac{1}{5} + (5 - \tfrac{37}{10})^2 \times \tfrac{2}{5} + (10 - \tfrac{37}{10})^2 \times \tfrac{1}{10}] \\
&= 7\cdot41 \text{ (pence)}^2,
\end{aligned}
$$

a longer calculation whether it is done with or without a hand calculator.

Using the same methods as those used for the results for the expected mean, the following results are obtained.

(i) If X is a discrete random variable and a and b are constants, then

$$\text{Var}(aX + b) = a^2 \text{Var}(X).$$

Proof

$$
\begin{aligned}
\text{Var}(aX + b) &= E(aX + b)^2 - (a\mu + b)^2 = E(a^2 X^2 + 2abX + b^2) - (a\mu + b)^2 \\
&= a^2 E(X^2) + 2abE(X) + b^2 - (a\mu + b)^2, \text{ since } a, b \text{ are} \\
&\quad \text{constants,}
\end{aligned}
$$

$$= a^2E(X^2) + 2ab\mu + b^2 - a^2\mu^2 - 2ab\mu - b^2,$$
$$= a^2[E(X^2) - \mu^2] = a^2\text{Var}(X).$$

Hence, if we take a linear function of the discrete random variable X, that is $(aX + b)$, where a, b are constants and X has mean μ, variance σ^2, then

$$E(aX + b) = a\mu + b, \ \text{Var}(aX + b) = a^2\sigma^2.$$

(ii) If X and Y are *independent* discrete random variables, then

$$\text{Var}(X \pm Y) = \text{Var}(X) + \text{Var}(Y).$$

Note here that, for the variances, the result is the addition of $\text{Var}(X)$ and $\text{Var}(Y)$ when we are taking the variance of the sum of X and Y and also when we are taking the variance of the difference of X and Y.

As in the case of $E(X \pm Y)$, it is too difficult for us to justify these results in this text. Again we illustrate the results by an example. To return to Example 3, on the die and the coin, X representing the outcome on the die and Y the outcome on the coin, the two random variables X and Y are independent in this case.

$\text{Var}(X) = \frac{1}{6}[1^2 + 2^2 + 3^2 + 4^2 + 5^2 + 6^2] - (\frac{7}{2})^2 = 2\frac{11}{12}.$
$\text{Var}(Y) = \frac{1}{2}[0^2 + 1^2] - (\frac{1}{2})^2 = \frac{1}{4}.$
$\text{Var}(X + Y) = \frac{1}{12}[2^2 + 3^2 + 4^2 + 5^2 + 6^2 + 7^2 + 1^2 + 2^2 + 3^2 + 4^2 + 5^2 + 6^2]$
$\qquad - (4)^2 = \frac{19}{6}.$
$\text{Var}(X - Y) = \frac{1}{12}[1^2 + 2^2 + 3^2 + 4^2 + 5^2 + 6^2 + 1^2 + 2^2 + 3^2 + 4^2 + 5^2] - (3)^2$
$\qquad = \frac{19}{6}.$

Hence,

$$\text{Var}(X + Y) = \text{Var}(X - Y) = \text{Var}(X) + \text{Var}(Y).$$

Exercise 2.2

1 Find, to two decimal places, the expectation $E(X)$, and the variance $\text{Var}(X)$, for each of the following distributions:

(a)

$X = x$	2	4	7
$p(x)$	$\frac{1}{3}$	$\frac{1}{2}$	$\frac{1}{6}$

(b)

$X = x$	-3	-1	2	4
$p(x)$	0·4	0·1	0·2	0·3

2 A distribution of positive integers has probability function

$$p(r) = \frac{1}{31}\binom{5}{r} \quad \text{for } r = 1, 2, 3, 4, 5,$$
$$p(r) = 0 \quad \text{for } r > 5.$$

Prove that the expected mean value is $\dfrac{80}{31}$ and that the variance is $\dfrac{1040}{961}$.

3   In a given business venture, a person can make a profit of £10 000 with probability 0·7, or take a loss of £6000 with probability 0·3. Find the person's expected gain.

4   Two boys are playing a game in which one boy tosses two fair coins. If he gets two 'heads', the other boy pays him 3p, if he gets only one 'head', the other boy pays him 2p, but if he gets no 'heads' he has to pay the other boy 5p. Find the expected winnings, on a toss, of the boy tossing the coins.

5   A fair coin is tossed until either one 'head' or four 'tails' occur. Find the expected number of tosses of the coin.

2.3   Continuous probability distributions

If X is a continuous random variable, we define $f(x)$, the *probability density function* (pdf) as the function satisfying the conditions

(i) $f(x) \geqslant 0$ for all $x \in S$, the sample space, and

(ii) $\displaystyle\int_S f(x)dx = 1. \left[\int_S \text{ means integration over the sample space.} \right]$

Further, we define, for any $x_0 < x_1$ in S,

$$P(x_0 < X < x_1) = \int_{x_0}^{x_1} f(x)dx,$$

and, hence, $P(x_0 < X < x_1)$ represents the area of the region under the graph of the probability density function $f(x)$ between the limits $x = x_0$ and $x = x_1$. Whenever X takes values only in some finite interval, we may assume that the pdf is zero elsewhere, so that we can write

$$\int_{-\infty}^{+\infty} f(x)dx = 1,$$

as a general result. Using this convention of the pdf being zero where it is not defined, we can then define $F(x)$, *the probability (cumulative) distribution function* by the relation

$$F(x_0) \equiv P(X \leqslant x_0) = \int_{-\infty}^{x_0} f(x)dx.$$

This represents the area of the region under the graph of the pdf, $f(x)$, from $x = -\infty$ to $x = x_0$. The function $F(x)$ obviously increases from zero at the bottom of the range to unity at the top of the range.

There is one special point which we must notice when X is a continuous random variable which does not arise when we deal with a discrete X. If we consider

$$P(x_0 < X < x_1) = \int_{x_0}^{x_1} f(x)dx,$$

and let x_0 approach x_1, then, in the limit, the integral on the right-hand side becomes zero. This means that, whereas we can speak of the probability that a discrete random variable is exactly x_0, there is no equivalent to this in the continuous random variable case, and we can speak only of the probability of X lying in a given interval. Certainly $f(x_0)$ does *not* represent the probability that X takes the value x_0. From the definition of $F(x)$ we see that $F(x_0)$ is the integral of $f(x)$ between the limits $x = -\infty$ and $x = x_0$, and hence,

$$f(x) = \frac{dF(x)}{dx}.$$

Example 5 The pdf of the continuous random variable X is given by

$$f(x) = kx^2, \quad 0 \leq x \leq 1,$$
$$f(x) = 0, \quad \text{elsewhere.}$$

Find (a) the value of k,
   (b) $P(X \leq \frac{1}{2})$,
   (c) $P(\frac{1}{4} < X < \frac{1}{2})$.

Illustrate the probability distribution by a sketch.

(a) $\displaystyle\int_{-\infty}^{+\infty} f(x)dx = 1 \Rightarrow \int_0^1 kx^2 dx = \frac{k}{3} = 1 \Rightarrow k = 3.$

(b) $\displaystyle P(X \leq \tfrac{1}{2}) = \int_{-\infty}^{1/2} f(x)dx = \int_0^{1/2} 3x^2 dx = \frac{1}{8}.$

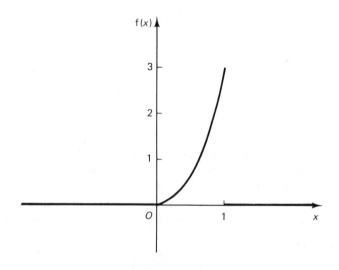

Fig. 2.3

(c) $P(\frac{1}{4} < X < \frac{1}{2}) = \int_{1/4}^{1/2} 3x^2 dx = \frac{7}{64}$.

The probability distribution is shown in Fig 2.3.

Just as we did for the discrete case, we can define $E(X)$ and $Var(X)$ when X is a continuous random variable, but now our definitions involve integrals rather than summation signs. We define

$$\mu \equiv E(X) = \int_{-\infty}^{+\infty} x f(x) dx,$$

the *expected mean value* of X, and

$$\sigma^2 \equiv Var(X) = \int_{-\infty}^{+\infty} (x - \mu)^2 f(x) dx,$$

the *variance* of X.

As before, we can assist in evaluating $Var(X)$ by using the result

$$Var(X) = \int_{-\infty}^{+\infty} x^2 f(x) dx - \mu^2.$$

Proof

$$\int_{-\infty}^{+\infty} (x - \mu)^2 f(x) dx = \int_{-\infty}^{+\infty} x^2 f(x) dx - 2\mu \int_{-\infty}^{+\infty} x f(x) dx + \mu^2 \int_{-\infty}^{+\infty} f(x) dx,$$

$$= \int_{-\infty}^{+\infty} x^2 f(x) dx - 2\mu^2 + \mu^2,$$

$$= \int_{-\infty}^{+\infty} x^2 f(x) dx - \mu^2,$$

since $\int_{-\infty}^{+\infty} x f(x) dx = \mu, \int_{-\infty}^{+\infty} f(x) dx = 1,$

or

$$Var(X) = \int_{-\infty}^{+\infty} x^2 f(x) dx - \mu^2 = E(X^2) - \mu^2.$$

Example 6 A random variable X has cumulative distribution function

$$F(x) = 0, \qquad x \leqslant 0,$$
$$F(x) = kx^4, \quad 0 < x \leqslant 2,$$
$$F(x) = 1, \qquad x > 2.$$

Find (a) $f(x)$, the pdf,
(b) $E(X)$,
(c) $Var(X)$.
Illustrate the probability density function by a sketch.

(a) $f(x) = \dfrac{dF(x)}{dx} = 4kx^3.$

$F(x)$ must be unity at $x = 2$,

$$\Rightarrow 16\,k = 1, \quad k = \frac{1}{16},$$

giving

$$f(x) = \frac{x^3}{4}, \quad 0 \leqslant x \leqslant 2,$$

$$f(x) = 0, \quad \text{elsewhere.}$$

(b) $E(X) = \displaystyle\int_{-\infty}^{+\infty} x f(x)\,dx = \int_0^2 \frac{x^3}{4}.x\,dx = \left[\frac{x^5}{20}\right]_0^2 = \frac{8}{5}.$

(c) $\mathrm{Var}(X) = \displaystyle\int_0^2 x^2 . \frac{x^3}{4}\,dx - \left(\frac{8}{5}\right)^2 = \left[\frac{x^6}{24}\right]_0^2 - \left(\frac{8}{5}\right)^2 = \frac{64}{24} - \frac{64}{25} = \frac{8}{75}.$

The probability density function is shown in Fig. 2.4.

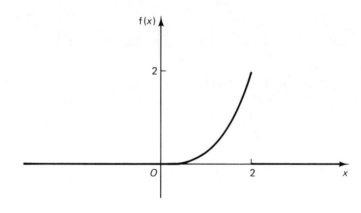

Fig. 2.4

Example 7 The continuous random variable X has pdf

$$f(x) = 2x/9, \quad 0 \leqslant x \leqslant 3,$$
$$f(x) = 0, \quad \text{elsewhere.}$$

(a) If two independent determinations of X are made, find the probability that both of them will be greater than 2.

(b) If three independent determinations of X are made, find the probability that two and only two of these are greater than 2.

[Note that since f(x) $\geqslant$ 0 and $\int_0^3 \frac{2x}{9}\,dx = \left[\frac{x^2}{9}\right]_0^3 = 1$, it follows that
f(x) = 2x/9, 0 $\leqslant$ x $\leqslant$ 3, does indeed represent a pdf.]

(a) $P(X > 2) = \int_2^3 \frac{2x}{9}\,dx = \frac{5}{9}$.

$P(X_1 \text{ and } X_2 > 2) = \frac{5}{9} \times \frac{5}{9} = \frac{25}{81}$, since the readings are independent.

(b) $P(X \ngtr 2) = 1 - \frac{5}{9} = \frac{4}{9}$.

$P(X_1, X_2 > 2, X_3 \ngtr 2) + P(X_1, X_3 > 2, X_2 \ngtr 2) + P(X_2, X_3 > 2, X_1 \ngtr 2)$

$= \frac{5}{9} \times \frac{5}{9} \times \frac{4}{9} \times 3 = \frac{100}{243}$.

Exercise 2.3

1 Given that X is a continuous random variable with pdf

$$f(x) = \tfrac{1}{4}x + k, \quad \text{for } 0 \leqslant x \leqslant 2,$$
$$f(x) = 0, \qquad\qquad \text{elsewhere},$$

find the value of k. Find also $P(\tfrac{1}{2} \leqslant X \leqslant 1)$.

2 The probability density function of a continuous random variable X is given by

$$f(x) = x(x - 1)(x - 3) \quad \text{for } 0 \leqslant x \leqslant 1,$$
$$f(x) = k \qquad\qquad\qquad \text{for } 1 < x \leqslant 3,$$
$$f(x) = 0 \qquad\qquad\qquad \text{otherwise},$$

where k is a suitable constant. Find the value of k. Find $E(X)$. Find also the probability that X is less than or equal to $E(X)$.

3 Find the distribution function $F(x)$ of the continuous random variable X whose probability density function is given by

$$f(x) = x/2 \qquad\qquad \text{for } 0 \leqslant x \leqslant 1,$$
$$f(x) = 1/2 \qquad\qquad \text{for } 1 < x \leqslant 2,$$
$$f(x) = (3 - x)/2 \quad \text{for } 2 < x \leqslant 3,$$
$$f(x) = 0 \qquad\qquad\;\; \text{elsewhere},$$

and illustrate $F(x)$ by a sketch.

4 The distribution function of the continuous random variable X is given by

$$F(x) = 1 - \frac{4}{x^2} \quad \text{for } x > 2,$$
$$F(x) = 0 \qquad\;\; \text{elsewhere}.$$

Find (a) $P(X > 4)$, (b) the pdf of X.

5 The time in minutes that the Inter-City train between two cities is early or late in arriving is a random variable with pdf given by

$$f(x) = \frac{3(16 - x^2)}{256} \quad \text{for } -4 < x < +4,$$

$$f(x) = 0 \qquad\qquad \text{elsewhere,}$$

where negative values of x indicate the train arriving early and positive values indicate the train arriving late. Find the probability that the train will arrive
(a) at least 2 minutes late,
(b) at least 1 minute early,
(c) between 1 and 3 minutes late.

Miscellaneous Exercise 2

1 An integer takes the value r with probability λr, λ being a contant, for $0 < r \leqslant 3n$; the probability is zero elsewhere. Find the value of λ and show that the expected mean value is $(6n + 1)/3$. Show also that the variance is $(3n + 2)(3n - 1)/18$.

[Note that $\displaystyle\sum_{r=1}^{n} r = n(n + 1)/2$,

$\displaystyle\sum_{r=1}^{n} r^2 = n(n + 1)(2n + 1)/6$,

$\displaystyle\sum_{r=1}^{n} r^3 = n^2(n + 1)^2/4$.]

2 When N people are inoculated it is known that each individual may experience an adverse reaction. Denote by X the number of people who react adversely. Assuming that the probability distribution of X is

$$P(X = r) = \frac{k}{2^r} \quad \text{for } r = 0, 1, \ldots, N,$$

where k is a positive constant, find k in terms of N. Find also, in terms of k and n, the probability that at least n of the people inoculated react adversely.

Show that, when $N = 5$, the probability of there being at least one adverse reaction is approximately 0.492.

3 A random variable R takes the integer value r with probability $P(r)$ defined by

$$P(r) = \lambda r \qquad\quad \text{for } r = 1, 2, 3, 4, 5,$$
$$P(r) = \lambda(11 - r) \quad \text{for } r = 6, 7, 8,$$
$$P(r) = 0 \qquad\qquad \text{for all other } r.$$

Find the value of the constant λ. Find also $E(R)$ and $\text{Var}(R)$. Represent the probability distribution of R on a suitable diagram. Write down the mean and variance of (a) $2R - 5$, (b) $5R_1 - 4R_2$, where R_1 and R_2 are independent observations of R.

4 The discrete random variable X has a probability function $P(X)$ defined by

$$P(0) = P(9) = \tfrac{1}{12},$$
$$P(1) = P(6) = \tfrac{1}{6},$$
$$P(4) = \tfrac{1}{2},$$
$$P(X) = 0 \quad \text{elsewhere.}$$

Draw a sketch to illustrate this probability distribution and find $E(X)$ and $\text{Var}(X)$. Find also $E(Y)$ and $\text{Var}(Y)$ when $Y = 5X - 3$.

5 The probability density function of the random variable X is given by

$$f(x) = 0 \quad \text{for } x < 0,$$
$$f(x) = cx \quad \text{for } 0 \leqslant x \leqslant 1,$$
$$f(x) = 0 \quad \text{for } x > 1,$$

where c is a positive constant. Find c, and evaluate $E(X)$.

6 The probability density function f of the random variable X is given by

$$f(x) = Ax^2(1 - x) \quad \text{for } 0 \leqslant x \leqslant 1,$$
$$f(x) = 0 \quad \text{elsewhere.}$$

(a) Evaluate A.
(b) Sketch the graph of $f(x)$.
(c) Find $E(X)$ and $\text{Var}(X)$.
(d) Calculate $P(X \leqslant \frac{1}{3})$.

7 The probability density function for the random variable X is given by

$$f(x) = k \sin x \quad \text{for } 0 \leqslant x \leqslant \pi,$$
$$f(x) = 0 \quad \text{for } x < 0 \text{ and } x > \pi.$$

Find (a) the value of k,
(b) $P(X \leqslant 2)$,
(c) $\text{Var}(X)$.

8 The random variable X has probability density function

$$f(x) = 1 \quad \text{for } 0 \leqslant x \leqslant k,$$
$$f(x) = \frac{1}{8} \quad \text{for } k < x \leqslant 2,$$
$$f(x) = 0 \quad \text{elsewhere.}$$

Find k and calculate $E(X)$ and $\text{Var}(X)$. Sketch the graph of the distribution function for this distribution.

9 A random variable X has probability density function f given by

$$f(x) = cx^k \quad \text{for } 0 \leqslant x \leqslant 1,$$
$$f(x) = 0 \quad \text{otherwise,}$$

where c and k are constants. Find an expression, in terms of k, for $E(X)$.

10 A random variable X takes only values x such that $k \leqslant x \leqslant 3$, and, in this range, $P(X \leqslant x) = \lambda(x - 1)(x + 3)(5 - x)$. Explain why $k = 1$. Calculate the value of λ and find $P(X \leqslant 2)$.

11 The pdf $f(x)$ of the continuous random variable X is given by

$$f(x) = b(cx - x^2) \quad \text{for } 0 \leqslant x \leqslant 2,$$
$$f(x) = 0 \quad \text{for } x < 0, x > 2,$$

where b and c are positive constants. Show that $c \geqslant 2$ and that $b = 3/(6c - 8)$.
Given that $E(X) = \frac{5}{4}$, calculate the values of b and c. Sketch the graph of $f(x)$ and find $\text{Var}(X)$.

12 The random variable X has probability density function $f(x)$ given by

$$f(x) = cx(x - 2)^2 \quad \text{for } 0 \leqslant x \leqslant 2,$$
$$f(x) = 0 \quad \text{elsewhere,}$$

where c is a constant. Find the value of c.
Find $E(X)$ and $\text{Var}(X)$. Show that $P(1 \leqslant X \leqslant 2)$ is approximately equal to $0 \cdot 31$.

13 The probability density function f(x) for the random variable X is defined by

$$f(x) = k(3 + 2x) \quad \text{for } 2 \leq x \leq 4,$$
$$f(x) = 0 \qquad\qquad \text{otherwise.}$$

Determine the value of k and sketch the graph of f(x).
  Calculate $E(X)$.
  Sketch the distribution function F(x).
  Calculate $P(2 \cdot 5 \leq X \leq 4)$, and find the value x_0 such that $P(X \leq x_0) = \frac{1}{4}$.

14 The continuous random variable X can assume values only between 0 and 4, and its pdf f(x) is given by $f(x) = k \sin(\pi x/4)$ for $0 \leq x \leq 4$. Find the values of k and of $E(X)$. Show that $\text{Var}(X) = 4[1 - (8/\pi^2)]$.

15 An ironmonger is supplied with paraffin once a week. The weekly demand, x hundred litres, has the continuous probability density function f(x), where $f(x) = 6(1 - x)^5$ for $0 \leq x \leq 1$. Find, to two decimal places, the required capacity of the paraffin tank if the probability that it will be exhausted in a given week does not exceed 0·01.

16 A point X is taken at random in a line PQ of length $2l$, all positions of the point being equally likely. Find the expected value of the product $PX . XQ$ and show that the probability that this product exceeds $l^2/4$ is $\sqrt{3}/2$.

3 Some discrete probability distributions

3.1 Introduction

There are some theoretical probability distributions that occur sufficiently frequently in statistical work to warrant individual consideration in our text. In this chapter we discuss four discrete probability distributions: uniform, binomial, geometric and Poisson.

3.2 The discrete uniform distribution

A discrete random variable X, whose probability function $p(r)$ is given by

$$p(r) = 1/k \quad \text{for } r = 1, 2, \ldots, k,$$
$$p(r) = 0 \quad \text{otherwise,}$$

where k is a constant integer, has a *discrete uniform distribution*. From the sketch of the distribution (Fig. 3.1) we can see why a uniform distribution is sometimes referred to as a *rectangular* distribution. We can find the expected mean of this distribution,

$$E(X) = \frac{1}{k}.1 + \frac{1}{k}.2 + \cdots + \frac{1}{k}.k$$
$$= \frac{1}{k}[1 + 2 + \cdots + k] = \frac{k(k + 1)}{k.2} = \frac{(k + 1)}{2},$$

since the sum of the first k natural numbers is equal to $[k(k + 1)]/2$. When we

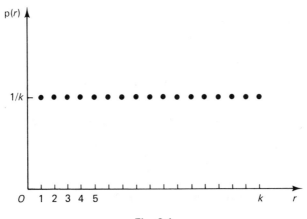

Fig. 3.1

look at the shape of the distribution as shown in Fig. 3.1, this is an obvious result for the mean.

The variance

$$\text{Var}(X) = \frac{1}{k}(1^2 + 2^2 + \cdots + k^2) - [E(X)]^2$$

$$= \frac{1}{k} \cdot \frac{k(k+1)(2k+1)}{6} - \frac{(k+1)^2}{4},$$

using the result that the sum of the squares of the first k natural numbers is $[k(k+1)(2k+1)]/6$,

$$\Rightarrow \text{Var}(X) = \frac{(2k^2 + 3k + 1)}{6} - \frac{(k^2 + 2k + 1)}{4} = \frac{k^2 - 1}{12}.$$

Example 1   An unbiased die is to be tossed repeatedly. Denoting by X the number which is the outcome of a throw, write down the probability function of X and find the mean and variance of X.

Since the die is unbiased, each of the numbers 1 to 6 has an equal chance of occurring, giving

$$P(X = r) \equiv p(r) = \frac{1}{6}, \quad r = 1, 2, 3, 4, 5, 6.$$

Here we have a discrete uniform distribution with $k = \frac{1}{6}$.

$$E(X) = \frac{6+1}{2} = \frac{7}{2}, \quad \text{Var}(X) = \frac{36-1}{12} = \frac{35}{12}.$$

Example 2   A boy tosses a fair die. If a non-prime number occurs, he will win that number of pence, but if a prime number occurs, he will forfeit that number of pence. Write down the possible outcomes (gain or loss) of a toss, with their respective probabilities, and hence find his expected gain or loss on one toss.

Let X pence be his gain or loss. Then X takes the values

$$-1, -2, -3, +4, -5, +6, \text{ each with probability of } \frac{1}{6},$$

since 1, 2, 3, 5 are prime; 4, 6 are not.

$$E(X) = -\frac{1}{6} - \frac{2}{6} - \frac{3}{6} + \frac{4}{6} - \frac{5}{6} + \frac{6}{6} = -\frac{1}{6}.$$

His expected loss is $\frac{1}{6}$ pence.

Exercise 3.2

1 A discrete uniform distribution is defined by $P(X = r) = 1/k$ for $r = 0, 1, \ldots,$ $(k - 1)$. Find the mean of the distribution and show that the variance is equal to $(k^2 - 1)/12$.

2 A girl is playing a game in which she tosses a fair die. If an even number occurs, she wins twice that number of pence, but if an odd number occurs, she forfeits three times that number of pence. Find her expected gain on one toss.

3 The discrete random variable X is known to be uniformly distributed over the set of consecutive integers $\{a, a + 1, \ldots, b\}$. Show that

$$E(X) = \frac{b + a}{2}, \quad Var(X) = \frac{(b - a)(b - a + 2)}{12}.$$

Given that $E(X) = 6$ and $Var(X) = 2$, find the values of a and b.

3.3 The binomial distribution

Suppose that we perform exactly n times an experiment which has only two possible outcomes, E or E'. We say that we have conducted n *trials* of the experiment. Given that each trial is independent of all the others and that the probability of the outcome E, $P(E)$, is constant and equal to p throughout the n trials, then we can find the probability of getting $0, 1, 2, \ldots, r, \ldots, n$, outcomes E in the n trials. Let the variable X represent the number of 'successes', or outcomes E, in the n trials. Then

$$\begin{aligned} P(X = 0) &= P(E' \cap E' \cap E' \ldots n \text{ times}) \\ &= P(E') \, P(E') \ldots n \text{ times, since the trials are independent,} \\ &= (1 - p)^n. \end{aligned}$$

For $P(X = 1)$ we must have the outcome E occurring once and the outcome E' occurring $(n - 1)$ times. However, the outcome E could occur on any one of the n trials, giving n ways in which the total of n outcomes could be arranged. Hence,

$$P(X = 1) = n(1 - p)^{n-1}p.$$

To generalise for $P(X = r)$, where $r \leqslant n$, we now have the outcome E occurring r times and the outcome E' occurring $(n - r)$ times. The r outcomes E could occur on any r of the n trials. Using the ideas of combinations, we can choose r places out of n in $\binom{n}{r}$ ways, where $\binom{n}{r} = \dfrac{n!}{r!(n - r)!}$.

Thus,

$$P(X = r) = \binom{n}{r}(1 - p)^{n-r}p^r, \ r = 0, 1, 2, \ldots, n.$$

These probabilities are also the consecutive $(n + 1)$ terms of the binomial expansion of $[(1 - p) + p]^n$, confirming that the total sum of the probabilities is $1^n = 1$ (certainty).

The distribution of X is called the *binomial distribution*, and we define it formally thus: The discrete random variable X having a probability function

$$P(X = r) \equiv P(r) = \binom{n}{r}(1 - p)^{n-r}p^r, \text{ where } 0 \leqslant p \leqslant 1, \text{ and } r = 0, 1, 2, \ldots, n,$$

is said to have a *binomial distribution*, $B(n,p)$.

We can write this $X \sim B(n,p)$, to be read as X is distributed binomially, with n independent trials and p the constant probability of 'success'.

The mean and variance of $B(n,p)$

$$E(X) = \sum_{r=0}^{n} r\binom{n}{r}(1 - p)^{n-r}p^r$$

$$= \sum_{r=1}^{n} \frac{r}{r!} \frac{n!}{(n - r)!}(1 - p)^{n-r}p^r, \text{ since the term when } r = 0$$

contributes zero to the sum,

$$= np\sum_{r=1}^{n} \frac{(n - 1)!}{(r - 1)![n - 1 - (r - 1)]!}(1 - p)^{(n-1)-(r-1)}p^{r-1}$$

$$= np\sum_{R=0}^{N} \frac{N!}{R!(N - R)!}(1 - p)^{N-R}p^R,$$

writing $N = n - 1$, $R = r - 1$ in the summation,

$$= np[(1 - p) + p]^N$$
$$= np.$$

We could have shortened this work a little by using the notation $q = 1 - p$, and we use this when finding $Var(X)$.

$$E(X^2) = \sum_{r=0}^{n} r^2\binom{n}{r}q^{n-r}p^r$$

$$= \sum_{r=1}^{n} [r(r - 1) + r]\binom{n}{r}q^{n-r}p^r,$$

since the term for which $r = 0$ contributes zero to the summation,

$$= \sum_{r=1}^{n} \frac{r(r - 1).n!}{(n - r)!r!}q^{n-r}p^r + \sum_{r=1}^{n} r\binom{n}{r}q^{n-r}p^r$$

$$= n(n - 1)p^2\sum_{r=2}^{n} \frac{(n - 2)!}{(r - 2)!(n - r)!}q^{n-r}p^{r-2} + np,$$

since the term for which $r = 1$ contributes zero to the first summation, and we have already shown, when finding $E(X)$, that the second summation is equal to np.

If we put $N = n - 2$, $R = r - 2$ in the first summation, we have

$$E(X^2) = n(n - 1)p^2 \sum_{R=0}^{N} \frac{N!}{R!(N - R)!} q^{N-R} p^R + np$$
$$= n(n - 1)p^2[q + p]^N + np$$
$$= n(n - 1)p^2 + np, \text{ since } q + p = 1,$$
$$\Rightarrow \text{Var}(X) = n(n - 1)p^2 + np - n^2 p^2$$
$$= np(1 - p) = npq.$$

A useful equality

In problems on the binomial distribution where we have to calculate more than one probability, a useful equality connects consecutive terms in a binomial expansion. It is

$$P(r + 1) = \frac{n - r}{r + 1} \cdot \frac{p}{1 - p} P(r).$$

For example, the value of $P(3)$ can be obtained from that of $P(2)$ by using the equality

$$P(3) = \frac{n - 2}{3} \cdot \frac{p}{1 - p} \cdot P(2),$$

where n and p will be given in the problem.

Example 3 It is known that 20% of the articles produced by a certain machine are defective. Given that a random sample of 10 articles produced by the machine is taken, find the probability that the sample will contain
(a) one defective article,
(b) less than two defective articles,
(c) at least three defective articles.

Let X be the number of defectives in the sample of 10 articles. Then X will have a binomial distribution with $n = 10$, and $p = 0.2$, since 20% of the articles are defective and we are calling the occurrence of a defective article a 'success'. We can write

$$X \sim B(10, 0.2).$$

(a) $P(X = 1) = \binom{10}{1}(1 - 0.2)^9 (0.2) \approx 0.268.$

(b) $P(X < 2) = P(0) + P(1)$
$$= (0.8)^{10} + 10(0.8)^9 (0.2) \approx 0.376.$$

(c) $P(X \geqslant 3) = P(3) + P(4) + \cdots + P(10),$
but this will involve many calculations. Instead, we will use

$$P(X \geqslant 3) = 1 - P(X < 3),$$

since the sum of all the probabilities is 1,

$$= 1 - P(0) - P(1) - P(2)$$
$$= 1 - (0 \cdot 8)^{10} - 10(0 \cdot 8)^9(0 \cdot 2) - \binom{10}{2}(0 \cdot 8)^8(0 \cdot 2)^2$$
$$\approx 0 \cdot 322.$$

Example 4   A fair die is to be tossed 1500 times. Given that the random variable X represents the number of times that a '4' occurs, find the mean and the variance of X. Write down the standard deviation of X.

Here we have $X \sim B(1500, \frac{1}{6})$, since the probability of getting a '4' is $\frac{1}{6}$ on each toss and there are 1500 independent tosses of the die.

Mean, $E(X) = np = 1500/6 = 250$.

Variance, $Var(X) = np(1 - p) = \dfrac{1500 \times 5}{6 \times 6} = 208\frac{1}{3}$.

Standard deviation $= \sqrt{(variance)} = \dfrac{25\sqrt{3}}{3}$.

Example 5   In a pole-vault competition, in order to enter the competition, each person is allowed not more than 3 attempts to jump once successfully a certain qualifying height. Given that p (a constant) is the probability of a person failing to jump that height successfully at any one attempt, find, in terms of p, the probability that a person will qualify to enter the competition.

   Given that people attempt to qualify to enter the competition in teams of 6 and that a team is considered as qualified to enter if at least 5 of the team have individually qualified, find, in terms of p, the probability of a team qualifying.

Let E represent the outcome that a person qualifies; that is, that a successful jump is achieved on the first or, if necessary, the second or third attempts. The probability of a successful jump is $(1 - p)$. Then

$$P(E) = (1 - p) + p(1 - p) + p^2(1 - p) = 1 - p^3.$$

This is the probability that a person qualifies, and so the probability that a person does not qualify, $P(E')$, is p^3. This is an obvious result, since, in order not to qualify, a person must fail on all three attempts.

   For a team of 6, we must find the probability of at least 5 of them individually qualifying — that is, either 5 or 6 qualifying. The distribution of the number of people in the team who individually qualify is $B(6, 1 - p^3)$.

$$\Rightarrow P(5) + P(6) = \binom{6}{5}p^3(1 - p^3)^5 + (1 - p^3)^6$$
$$= 6p^3(1 - p^3)^5 + (1 - p^3)^6$$
$$= (1 - p^3)^5(6p^3 + 1 - p^3)$$
$$= (1 - p^3)^5(1 + 5p^3).$$

Exercise 3.3

1   In a large collection of seeds, 3 out of 4 are lupins and the rest are weeds. If they are planted at random, find, to two decimal places, the probability that in a row of 5 plants
   (a) all are lupins,
   (b) at least 4 are lupins.

2   Two girls, Alice and Brenda, play a game in which Alice should win 6 games to every 5 won by Brenda. If they play 4 games, find, to two decimal places, the probability that Alice will win at least 2 games.

3   After batteries have been stored in a certain climate, it is found that an average of one-fifth of them are flat. A shopkeeper buys 3 batteries. Find the probability that exactly 2 of them are not flat.
   A man buying batteries wishes there to be a probability of at least 0·95 that at least 2 of them are not flat. Find whether 4 will be enough for him to buy.

4   A box contains 12 black counters and 8 white counters. Calculate the probability that a random sample of 5 counters drawn together from the box will contain at least 4 black counters.

5   On average rain falls on 12 days in every 30. Find the probability
   (a) that the first 4 days of a given week will be fine and the remainder wet,
   (b) that rain will fall on just 4 days of a given week.

3.4   The geometric distribution

A discrete random variable X with probability function

$$P(X = r) = (1 - p)^r p \quad \text{where } 0 \leqslant p \leqslant 1 \text{ and } r = 0, 1, 2, \ldots,$$

is said to have a *geometric distribution with parameter p*.

This distribution can arise in an experiment which fulfils the conditions which are required to be satisfied for the binomial distribution $B(n,p)$ except that, instead of counting the number of 'successes' which occur in the n trials, as we did for $B(n,p)$, we carry on with the trials only until we get one 'success'. Given that X is defined as the number of 'failures' we get before we get a 'success', then

$$P(X = r) = (1 - p)^r p,$$

since the probability of 'failure' is $(1 - p)$. Thus, X has a geometric distribution.

This distribution can be shown to have a mean $E(X) = (1 - p)/p$, and variance $Var(X) = (1 - p)/p^2$. You are asked to obtain these results in Exercise 3.4, Nos. 1 and 5.

Example 6   A die is to be thrown until a '3' is obtained. Given that X is the total number of throws needed to obtain the '3', write down the probability function of X. Find
(a) the most probable number of throws,

(b) the mean number of throws,
(c) the least value n of X such that the probability that a '3' has been thrown on or before the nth toss is greater than $0 \cdot 5$.

$P(X = r) = \left(\frac{5}{6}\right)^{r-1}\left(\frac{1}{6}\right)$ for $r = 1, 2, \ldots$.
(a) The greatest value of $P(X = r)$ over the sample space occurs when $r = 1$ (that is, 'no failures'), giving $P(1) = \frac{1}{6}$.
(b) The mean number of failures is $(1 - p)/p$, and $p = \frac{1}{6}$,

$$\Rightarrow \text{mean} = 5 \text{ failures} - \text{that is, 6 tosses altogether.}$$

(c) $P(X \leqslant n) = \frac{1}{6}\left[\left(\frac{5}{6}\right)^0 + \left(\frac{5}{6}\right)^1 + \left(\frac{5}{6}\right)^2 + \cdots + \left(\frac{5}{6}\right)^{n-1}\right]$

$$= \frac{1}{6} \frac{\left[1 - \left(\frac{5}{6}\right)^n\right]}{\left(1 - \frac{5}{6}\right)},$$

using the result for a geometric progression

$$\sum_{s=0}^{n-1} r^s = \frac{1 - r^n}{1 - r},$$

$$\Rightarrow P(X \leqslant n) = 1 - \left(\frac{5}{6}\right)^n.$$

We require

$$1 - \left(\frac{5}{6}\right)^n > 0 \cdot 5$$
$$\Rightarrow \qquad \left(\frac{5}{6}\right)^n < 0 \cdot 5$$
$$\Rightarrow \qquad 2 < \left(\frac{6}{5}\right)^n \Rightarrow n \lg(1 \cdot 2) > \lg 2,$$
$$\Rightarrow \qquad n > 3 \cdot 802.$$

The least value of n is, therefore, 4, since n must be an integer.

Exercise 3.4

1   The probability distribution of a random variable X is geometric; that is, $P(X = r) = (1 - p)^r p$, for $r = 0, 1, 2, \ldots$, where $0 < p < 1$. Given that

$$\sum_{n=1}^{\infty} n p^{n-1} = \frac{1}{(1 - p)^2},$$

show that $E(X) = (1 - p)/p$.

2   A random variable X is distributed geometrically. Given that $P(X = 0) = \frac{3}{4}$, illustrate on graph paper the distribution for $0 \leqslant X \leqslant 4$.

3   In a game, the player throws a coin until a 'head' is obtained and he then receives from the bank $\pounds 2^n$, where n is the number of throws. Find the probability that he receives (a) £16, (b) more than £16. Find the probability that, if the bank holds $\pounds 10^5$, the player will break the bank in a single play.

4   If the probability is $0 \cdot 7$ that a learner driver will pass the driving test on any given attempt, find, to two significant figures, the probability that a person will pass his test on his fourth attempt. (You may assume that the attempts are all independent.)

5 Show that the variance of the geometric distribution with probability function

$$P(X = R) = (1 - p)^R p \quad \text{for } R = 0, 1, 2, \ldots,$$

is equal to $(1 - p)/p^2$.

[*Hint*: Differentiate twice, with respect to p, both sides of the equation for the sum of the infinite geometric series

$$\sum_{R=0}^{\infty} (1 - p)^R = \frac{1}{p}, \text{ where } 0 < p < 1.]$$

3.5 The Poisson distribution

A discrete random variable X with probability function

$$P(X = r) = \frac{\mu^r e^{-\mu}}{r!}, \quad r = 0, 1, 2, \ldots,$$

where μ is a constant, is said to have a *Poisson distribution with parameter* μ. This distribution was first given by S. D. Poisson in 1837. He derived it as the limit of a binomial distribution $B(n,p)$ when n tends to infinity and p tends to 0 in such a manner that np remains constant and equal to μ. The derivation of this limit is not within the scope of this text but we will show how this limiting distribution can be used.

If we need to calculate probabilities for $B(n,p)$ when n is large, the arithmetic is very lengthy, although tables of binomial coefficients and of cumulative binomial probabilities can be obtained. However, in general, the Poisson distribution will provide, with less arithmetic, a good approximation to the binomial probabilities for large values of n and small values of p; for example, when $n \geqslant 20$ and $p \leqslant 0.05$, and when $n \geqslant 50$ and $p \leqslant 0.1$. For any given small value of p, the larger n is, the more accurate will be the approximation.

By applying the same limiting conditions to the mean and variance of $B(n,p)$, we can derive expressions for the mean and variance of the Poisson distribution. For the binomial, we had mean np, variance $np(1 - p)$. We know that $\mu = np$, and, hence, in the limit, as $p \to 0$, we have, for the Poisson distribution,

$$\text{mean } E(X) = \mu,$$
$$\text{Var}(X) = \mu(1 - p) \to \mu.$$

For the Poisson distribution, then, the mean and the variance are equal, both being equal to the parameter μ.

So far we have considered the Poisson distribution as an approximation to $B(n,p)$ for small values of p and large values of n. There is another way in which the Poisson distribution may occur. It can be shown by mathematical argument that, if X is the number of events that occur in an interval of fixed length, then X has a Poisson distribution provided that the events occur

(a) singly,
(b) independently of one another,
(c) uniformly — that is, the expected number of events in a given interval is proportional to the size of the interval, and,
(d) at random in continuous space or time.

There are many examples for which the Poisson distribution is a good model. For example, the number of flaws in a length of cloth, the number of sultanas in a cake, the number of telephone calls coming into an exchange in a certain length of time, the number of α-particles emitted per unit time from a radioactive source.

Example 7   On average, 1% of the lenses being produced by a machine are faulty. Estimate the probability that a random sample of 100 lenses taken from the production of this machine will contain
(a) not more than 1 faulty lens,
(b) more than 2 faulty lenses.

Let X represent the number of faulty lenses. Then $X \sim B(100, 0 \cdot 01)$, since the probability of a faulty lens is $0 \cdot 01$ and the sample size is 100. We can approximate this by a Poisson distribution with

$$\mu = np = 100 \times 0 \cdot 01 = 1.$$

(a) $P(X \not> 1) = P(0) + P(1) = e^{-1} + 1 . e^{-1} = 2e^{-1} \approx 0 \cdot 736.$
(b) $P(X > 2) = P(3) + P(4) + \ldots$.
The right-hand side of this requires an infinity of probabilities to be evaluated, which is not practicable. Instead, we must use

$$P(X > 2) = 1 - P(0) - P(1) - P(2)$$
$$= 1 - e^{-1} - 1 . e^{-1} - \frac{1^2 . e^{-1}}{2}$$
$$= 1 - \frac{5e^{-1}}{2} \approx 0 \cdot 080.$$

Example 8   Large rolls of velvet are being produced on a loom. The number of imperfections per 3 m of the velvet is a random variable having a Poisson distribution with $\mu = 2 \cdot 3$. Find the probability that 3 m of the velvet chosen at random from the roll will have
(a) 3 imperfections,
(b) at most 2 imperfections.
Write down the variance of the distribution.

Here X, the number of imperfections per 3 m of velvet, has a Poisson distribution parameter $2 \cdot 3$.

(a) $P(X = 3) = \dfrac{e^{-2 \cdot 3}(2 \cdot 3)^3}{3!} = 0 \cdot 203$ to three decimal places.

(b) $P(X \leqslant 2) = P(0) + P(1) + P(2) = e^{-2 \cdot 3}(1 + 2 \cdot 3 + (2 \cdot 3)^2/2)$
$$= 0 \cdot 596 \text{ to three decimal places.}$$
Variance = mean = $2 \cdot 3$.

Example 9 The number of bacteria in 1 ml of inoculum is known to follow a Poisson distribution with mean $3 \cdot 1$. If at least 3 bacteria are required for a 1 ml dose to cause infection, show that the probability of a dose causing infection is approximately equal to $0 \cdot 6$.

Calculate the probability that, if 6 doses are administered, at least 2 of them will cause infection.

The probability of a dose causing infection is the probability of having 3 or more bacteria.

$$P(\geqslant 3) = 1 - P(0) - P(1) - P(2)$$
$$= 1 - e^{-3 \cdot 1}(1 + 3 \cdot 1 + (3 \cdot 1)^2/2)$$
$$= 1 - 0 \cdot 41 \approx 0 \cdot 6.$$

Six doses are administered with probability $0 \cdot 6$ of a single dose causing infection. If X is the number of doses causing infection, then $X \sim B(6, 0 \cdot 6)$.

$$P(\geqslant 2) = 1 - (0 \cdot 4)^6 - 6(0 \cdot 4)^5(0 \cdot 6) = 1 - 4(0 \cdot 4)^5$$
$$= 1 - 0 \cdot 041 \approx 0 \cdot 96.$$

Exercise 3.5

1 Telephone calls coming into a switchboard follow a Poisson distribution with mean 2 per minute. Find the probability that in a given minute there will be 4 or more calls.

2 The road accidents in a certain area occur at an average rate of 1 every 3 days. Calculate, to three decimal places, the probability of 0, 1, 2, $\ldots$, 5 accidents per week in the district. Obtain the most likely number of accidents per week.

3 An airline finds that, on average, 3% of the persons who reserve seats for a certain flight do not turn up for the flight. Consequently, the airline decides to allow 200 people to reserve seats on a plane which can only accommodate 196 passengers. Find the probability that there will be a seat available for every person who has reserved a seat and who turns up for the flight.

4 In an examination 70% of the candidates pass but only 3% obtain Grade A. Use the binomial distribution to estimate the probability that a random group of 9 candidates will contain at most 2 failures. Use the Poisson distribution to estimate the probability that a random group of 50 candidates will contain not more than one with Grade A.

5 In the manufacture of radio sets, on the average 1 set in 25 is defective. Use the Poisson distribution to estimate the probability that a consignment of 100 radio sets will contain

(a) no defective set,

(b) fewer than 4 defective sets.

A random sample of 25 of the radio sets is found to contain 3 defectives. Is it likely that on average only 1 radio set in 25 is defective?

6 Two hundred misprints are distributed randomly throughout a book of 600 pages. Find the probability that a given page will contain

(a) exactly 2 misprints,

(b) 2 or more misprints.

7 In a trial, 7 coins are tossed together. Given that 100 trials are made, find the number of times one should expect to obtain 5 'heads' and 2 'tails'.

8 For the Poisson distribution with probability function

$$P(X = r) = \frac{\mu^r e^{-\mu}}{r!}, \quad r = 0, 1, 2, \ldots,$$

where μ is a constant, show that $E(X) = \mu$.

Show also that $Var(X) = \mu$.

$$\left[Hint: \text{Write } \sum_1^\infty \frac{r^2 \mu^r e^{-\mu}}{r!} = \sum_1^\infty \frac{r(r-1)\mu^r e^{-\mu}}{r!} + \sum_1^\infty \frac{r\mu^r e^{-\mu}}{r!}. \right]$$

Miscellaneous Exercise 3

1 In a game a player cannot start until he has thrown a '6' on a die. Calculate the probability that he has to throw the die more than 3 times before he can start.

2 A die is thrown repeatedly until a '6' is thrown. Given that an odd number of throws is required, calculate, to three significant figures, the probability that 3 throws are required.

3 A large batch of earthenware mugs is moulded and fired. After firing, a random sample of 10 mugs is inspected for flaws before glazing, decoration and final firing. Given that 25% of the mugs in the batch have flaws, use the appropriate binomial distribution to calculate, to two significant figures, the probability that the random sample contains

(a) no mugs with flaws,

(b) exactly 1 mug with a flaw.

The batch is accepted without further checking if the random sample contains no more than 2 mugs with flaws. Find the probability that the batch will be accepted without further checking.

4 A gun is firing at a target and it must make at least 2 direct hits. The probability of a direct hit with a single round is $\frac{1}{4}$, and this probability remains constant throughout the firing. Four rounds are fired, and, if at least 2 direct hits are scored, firing ceases. Otherwise, 4 more rounds are fired. Find the probability that at least 2 direct hits are scored

(a) only 4 rounds being fired,

(b) 8 rounds having to be fired.

5 An examination consists of 9 questions in each of which the candidate must say which one of 5 answers is the correct one. For each question a certain candidate guesses any one of the 5 answers with equal probability.

(a) Prove that the probability that he obtains more than 1 correct answer is equal to $\dfrac{5^9 - 13 \times 4^8}{5^9}$.

(b) Find the probability that he obtains correct answers to 7 or more questions.

6 State clearly the conditions under which a binomial distribution applies.

A man canvasses people to join a book club. For each new member he receives £1. The probability that a person he canvasses will join is 0·15. Calculate, to three decimal places, the probability that he will obtain 3 or more new members from 10 people canvassed. State the amount of money that he would be expected to obtain on average from 20 canvassings. State how many people he would need to canvass each evening to average 3 new members per evening. Calculate the minimum number of people he must arrange to canvass to be 99% certain of obtaining at least one new member.

7 Write down an expression for $P(X = r)$, where X is the number of successes in 20 independent trials each having a probability of 0·05 of success. Write down the values of $E(X)$ and $\mathrm{Var}\,(X)$.

A large batch of cigarette lighters is accepted if either
(a) a random sample of 20 lighters contains no defective lighter, or
(b) a random sample of 20 lighters contains one defective lighter only, and a second sample of 20 is then drawn and found to contain no defective lighter.
Otherwise, the batch is rejected. If, in fact, 5% of the lighters in the batch are defective, find the probability of the batch being accepted. Find the expected number of lighters that will have to be sampled to reach a decision on a batch.

8 In the mass production of plug sockets it is found that, on average, one in 30 plug sockets is defective. Assuming that the number of defectives in a random sample of plug sockets follows a Poisson distribution, show that there is a probability of approximately 0·05 that a random sample of 60 plug sockets will contain more than 4 defectives and a probability of less than 0·01 that it will contain more than 6 defectives.

9 Random samples, each of volume 1 cm^3, are taken from a well-mixed cell suspension in which, on average, 1 cell of type A is present per cm^3. Find the probability that a sample will contain fewer than 3 cells of type A. Given that 10 such samples are taken, find the probability that exactly 4 of these will contain fewer than 3 type A cells.

10 At a factory, 15% of the cassette players made are defective. Find the probability that a sample of 5 cassette players will contain
(a) no defective,
(b) exactly 1 defective,
(c) at least 2 defectives.

11 In a laboratory experiment, an untrained mouse can pass through 3 doors, behind only 1 of which is food. It goes through the doors until it finds the food. Assuming that the mouse has no memory and that it chooses the doors at random, write down the probability distribution for the number of doors it tries in order to get the food.

A mouse which has been trained in the experiment is thought to have developed a memory so that it will not try any door more than once. Assuming this is true, write down the corresponding probability distribution for the trained mouse.
Find the probability that
(a) the trained mouse will obtain food with fewer doors tried than the untrained mouse,
(b) the untrained mouse will obtain food with fewer doors tried than the trained mouse.

12 In a large batch of dried fruit, it is known that the average proportion of sultanas

is 0·55 and the average proportion of pieces of candied peel is 0·005. Calculate to three decimal places

(a) the probability of there being 2 or more sultanas in a random sample of 10 of the dried fruits,

(b) the probability of there being 3 or fewer pieces of candied peel in a random sample of 400 of the dried fruits.

13 The number of bacteria in a dose of 1 ml is known to follow a Poisson distribution with mean 3·5. If at least 3 bacteria are needed for a dose to cause infection, show that the probability of a dose of 1 ml causing infection is approximately 0·679. Find the probability of infection being caused if the dose is trebled.

14 A single die is thrown 6 times. Find the probability that

(a) at least one '6' is thrown,

(b) fewer than two '6's are thrown,

(c) each face of the die turns up once.

Find also the probability that, when a die is thrown repeatedly, a '6' appears for the first time at the kth throw.

Find the least value of k such that there is more than a 60% chance of obtaining a '6' on the kth throw or earlier, and find the values of $E(k)$ and $Var(k)$.

15 Failures of the steering mechanism of a car occur at random with, on average, 1 failure in 300 000 miles. Use the Poisson distribution to find, to four decimal places, the probability that

(a) the car completes 45 000 miles without a steering failure,

(b) there are 3 or more failures in 45 000 miles.

Two cars, X and Y, with this type of steering mechanism, are bought, and, while X is running its first 45 000 miles, Y will run 150 000 miles. Find the probability that during this period there will be not more than one steering failure altogether.

16 An examination paper consists of 20 questions, to each of which the candidate has to answer 'True' or 'False'. A candidate answers the paper entirely by guessing — that is, he chooses the answers 'True' and 'False' with equal probability. Each question carries equal marks. Use a table of cumulative binomial probabilities to show that, if the pass mark is 75%, the probability that he passes is approximately 0·021.

4 Some continuous probability distributions

We now discuss three continuous probability distributions that occur frequently in statistical work: the uniform, the exponential and the normal distributions.

4.1 The continuous uniform distribution

A continuous random variable X whose probability density function (pdf) is given by

$$f(x) = \frac{1}{b-a} \quad \text{for } a \leqslant x \leqslant b, \text{ where } a, b \text{ are finite,}$$

$$f(x) = 0 \quad \text{otherwise,}$$

has a *continuous uniform distribution over the interval* $[a, b]$. We can see that this is a valid density function, since $f(x) \geqslant 0$, and

$$\int_{-\infty}^{+\infty} f(x)dx = \int_a^b \frac{1}{b-a}\,dx = 1.$$

The mean of the distribution, $E(X)$, is given by

$$E(X) = \int_{-\infty}^{+\infty} xf(x)dx = \frac{1}{b-a}\int_a^b x\,dx = \frac{a+b}{2},$$

an obvious result when we consider the sketch of $f(x)$ as shown in Fig. 4.1.

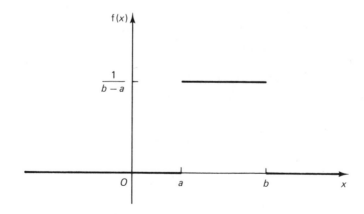

Fig. 4.1

The variance of the distribution is given by

$$\begin{aligned}
\text{Var}(X) &= E(X^2) - [E(X)]^2 \\
&= \int_a^b \frac{x^2}{b-a}\,dx - \frac{(a+b)^2}{4} \\
&= \frac{b^3 - a^3}{3(b-a)} - \frac{(a+b)^2}{4} \\
&= \frac{b^2 + ab + a^2}{3} - \frac{a^2 + 2ab + b^2}{4} \\
&= \frac{b^2 - 2ab + a^2}{12} = \frac{(b-a)^2}{12}.
\end{aligned}$$

The distribution function is given by

$$F(x) = 0 \quad \text{for } x < a,$$
$$F(x) = \int_a^x \frac{1}{b-a}\,dx = \frac{x-a}{b-a} \quad \text{for } a \leqslant x \leqslant b,$$
$$F(x) = 1 \quad \text{for } x > b.$$

This distribution has the property that the probability of X lying in any range within $[a, b]$ is the same as the probability of X lying in any other range *of the same length* in $[a, b]$. It can be used as a model for the rounding errors made when measurements are taken. For example, if we are measuring to the nearest millimetre and we may assume that the rounding error is equally likely to take any value between -0.5 mm and $+0.5$ mm, then we may take the uniform distribution over $[-0.5, +0.5]$ as a reasonable model for the distribution of the rounding errors. Alternatively, one might assume that certain fibres, which are being tested for strength, break along their lengths at a distance X from one end, where X has a uniform distribution, and then this model could be tested against experimental results.

Example 1   The hardness on the Brinell scale of certain magnesium alloys is assumed to follow a continuous uniform distribution over the interval [27,80]. Write down the pdf, and find the mean and the variance of the distribution.

$$f(x) = \frac{1}{80-27} = \frac{1}{53} \quad \text{for } 27 \leqslant x \leqslant 80,$$
$$f(x) = 0 \quad \text{otherwise.}$$
$$E(X) = \frac{80+27}{2} = 53.5.$$
$$\text{Var}(X) = \frac{(80-27)^2}{12} = \frac{2809}{12} \approx 234.1.$$

Example 2   A point is chosen at random on the line segment [1,3]. Find the probability that the point will lie between 1·5 and 2.

Let X represent the point; then X is equally likely to take any value in $[1,3]$, since it is chosen at random. Hence, X is uniformly distributed on $[1,3]$ with pdf

$$f(x) = \frac{1}{3-1} = \frac{1}{2} \quad \text{for } 1 \le x \le 3,$$
$$f(x) = 0 \quad \text{otherwise.}$$
$$P(1 \cdot 5 < X < 2) = \int_{1 \cdot 5}^{2} \tfrac{1}{2} dx = \tfrac{1}{4}.$$

Example 3   A point is chosen at random on a line of length a. Find the probability that the ratio of the length of the shorter segment to the length of the longer segment is less than $\tfrac{1}{3}$.

Let X represent the distance from the point to one end of the line, so that the length of the other part is $(a - X)$. Then X is uniformly distributed with pdf

$$f(x) = \frac{1}{a} \quad \text{for } 0 \le x \le a,$$
$$f(x) = 0 \quad \text{otherwise.}$$

Then either

$$\frac{X}{a-X} < \frac{1}{3} \Rightarrow X < \frac{a}{4},$$
$$P\left(X < \frac{a}{4}\right) = F\left(\frac{a}{4}\right) = \frac{1}{a} \cdot \frac{a}{4} = \frac{1}{4}.$$

or

$$\frac{a-X}{X} < \frac{1}{3} \Rightarrow X > \frac{3a}{4},$$
$$P\left(X > \frac{3a}{4}\right) = 1 - F\left(\frac{3a}{4}\right) = 1 - \frac{3}{4} = \frac{1}{4}.$$
$$\Rightarrow \text{probability} = \frac{1}{4} + \frac{1}{4} = \frac{1}{2}.$$

This is an obvious result if we look at Fig. 4.2. We have found that the point may lie on AC or on DB, but not on CD; that is, it may lie on half of the line AB. Hence, the probability is $\dfrac{\frac{1}{2}AB}{AB} = \dfrac{1}{2}$.

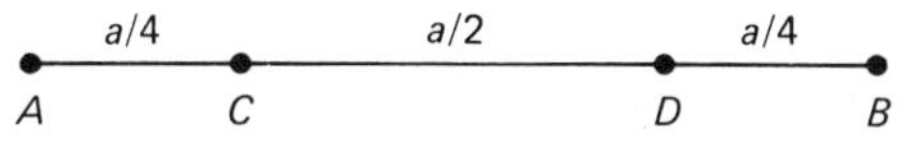

Fig. 4.2

Exercise 4.1

1 X is a continuous random variable with pdf f(x), where

$$f(x) = \tfrac{1}{8} \quad \text{for } 0 \leqslant x \leqslant 8,$$
$$f(x) = 0 \quad \text{elsewhere.}$$

Calculate $P(2 \leqslant X \leqslant 6)$. Find $F(x)$, the distribution function, and illustrate $F(x)$ by a sketch.

2 Given that X is a continuous random variable uniformly distributed with pdf f(x), where

$$f(x) = k \quad \text{for } 2 \leqslant x \leqslant 4,$$
$$f(x) = 0 \quad \text{elsewhere,}$$

find the values of k and of $E(X)$ and $Var(X)$.
Determine the distribution function $F(x)$, and illustrate $F(x)$ by a sketch.

3 A continuous random variable X has a probability density function f(x) given by

$$f(x) = k \quad \text{for } 0 \leqslant x \leqslant 4,$$
$$f(x) = 0 \quad \text{elsewhere.}$$

Find the value of k, and determine the distribution function $F(x)$. Evaluate $P(X \leqslant 3)$.

4 The random variable X has a continuous uniform distribution over the interval $[a,b]$. Prove that the probability that X will take values less than $a + m(b - a)$ is equal to m, given that $0 \leqslant m \leqslant 1$.

4.2 The exponential distribution

A continuous random variable X whose pdf f(x) is given by

$$f(x) = \lambda e^{-\lambda x} \quad \text{for } x \geqslant 0, \text{ where } \lambda \text{ is a positive constant,}$$
$$f(x) = 0 \quad \text{otherwise,}$$

has an *exponential distribution with parameter* λ. Since

$$\int_{-\infty}^{+\infty} f(x)dx = \int_0^\infty \lambda e^{-\lambda x} dx = \left[-e^{-\lambda x} \right]_0^\infty = 1, \text{ for } \lambda > 0,$$

and $f(x) \geqslant 0$, this is a valid density function.

$$E(X) = \int_0^\infty \lambda x e^{-\lambda x} dx$$

$$= \left[-x e^{-\lambda x} \right]_0^\infty + \int_0^\infty e^{-\lambda x} dx, \text{ integrating by parts,}$$

$$= \left[\frac{e^{-\lambda x}}{-\lambda} \right]_0^\infty = \frac{1}{\lambda}, \text{ for } \lambda > 0.$$

$$E(X^2) = \int_0^\infty \lambda x^2 e^{-\lambda x} dx$$

$$= \left[-x^2 e^{-\lambda x} \right]_0^\infty + 2 \int_0^\infty x e^{-\lambda x} dx, \text{ integrating by parts,}$$

$$= \frac{2}{\lambda} E(X) = \frac{2}{\lambda^2}.$$

$$\Rightarrow \text{Var}(X) = \frac{2}{\lambda^2} - \frac{1}{\lambda^2} = \frac{1}{\lambda^2}.$$

The distribution function, $F(x)$, is given by

$$F(x) = 0 \text{ for } x < 0,$$

$$F(x) = \int_0^x \lambda e^{-\lambda x} dx = \left[-e^{-\lambda x} \right]_0^x = 1 - e^{-\lambda x}, \text{ for } x \geq 0.$$

Many real-life situations can be modelled by an exponential distribution. For example, suppose that a machine is testing a particular electrical component. Let T represent the length of time that a component in continuous use lasts before it fails. If T has a constant failure rate — that is, after a component is in use its probability of failing does not change (there is no wearing effect) — then T can be modelled by an exponential distribution.

The waiting time between events in a Poisson process will have an exponential distribution, with parameter λ having the same value as the respective Poisson parameter μ, provided that the units of time are the same in both distributions. For example, the time interval between vehicles passing a certain point when traffic is flowing freely, each vehicle travelling independently of (that is, not restricted by) any other vehicle, can be considered as an exponential variable.

An interesting property of the exponential distribution is that it has 'no memory'. That is, suppose that event E has not occurred during time T; then the probability that it does not occur during the following interval of time t is the same as the probability that it would not have occurred during time t from the start. Expressed in symbolic form, this is

$$P(X > T + t | X > T) = P(X > t).$$

In other words, the property of 'no occurrence' during the first T units of time is 'forgotten' so far as the subsequent time t is concerned.

Proof

$$P(X > T + t | X > T) = \frac{P(X > T + t)}{P(X > T)} = \frac{1 - F(T + t)}{1 - F(T)}.$$

We have shown that $F(x) = 1 - e^{-\lambda x}$ and, hence,

$$P(X > T + t | X > T) = \frac{e^{-\lambda(T + t)}}{e^{-\lambda T}} = e^{-\lambda t}$$

$$= P(X > t).$$

This same property of 'no memory' can also be shown to apply to the geometric distribution discussed in Chapter 3.

Example 4 The mileage, in thousands of miles, before tyre replacement is necessary in lorries using a certain cross-ply tyre is a random variable which has an exponential distribution with parameter $\frac{1}{60}$. State the mean mileage, and find the probability that a tyre of this type will last for
(a) at most 20 000 miles,
(b) more than 40 000 miles.

$$E(X) = \frac{1}{\lambda} = 60 \Rightarrow \text{mean mileage is } 60\,000 \text{ miles.}$$

The exponential distribution function gives

$$P(X \leqslant M) = 1 - e^{-M/60}, \text{ where } M \text{ is the mileage in thousands of miles.}$$

(a) $P(X \leqslant 20) = 1 - e^{-20/60} = 1 - e^{-1/3} \approx 0\cdot283$.
(b) $P(X > 40) = 1 - P(X \leqslant 40) = e^{-40/60} = e^{-2/3} \approx 0\cdot513$.

Example 5 Given that the length of the life of a light-bulb of a certain type is an exponentially distributed random variable with expected lifetime of 15 weeks when continuously lit, find the probability that, if 3 such bulbs are lit at the same time and left alight, at least 2 of them will still be alight after 20 weeks.

X, the length of life in weeks, is distributed exponentially with parameter λ, given by $\frac{1}{\lambda} = 15, \lambda = \frac{1}{15}$.

$$f(x) = \frac{e^{-x/15}}{15} \text{ for } x \geqslant 0.$$

$$F(x) = 1 - e^{-x/15}.$$
$$P(X < 20) = F(20) = 1 - e^{-20/15} = 1 - e^{-4/3}$$
$$\Rightarrow P(X \geqslant 20) = 1 - P(X < 20) = e^{-4/3}, \text{ for each bulb.}$$

Hence, the probability that at least 2 of the 3 bulbs are still alight is given by the sum of the probabilities that only 2 are alight and that all 3 are alight.

$$= 3e^{-4/3}.e^{-4/3}(1 - e^{-4/3}) + e^{-4/3}.e^{-4/3}.e^{-4/3}$$
$$= e^{-8/3}(3 - 2e^{-4/3}) \approx 0\cdot172.$$

Example 6 The time, T seconds, between the arrival of successive vehicles at a point on a country road has pdf given by $f(t) = \lambda e^{-\lambda t}$ when $t \geqslant 0$, and where $\lambda = \frac{1}{100}$. State the mean and variance of T.

A pedestrian takes 50 seconds to cross the road at this point. Find the probability that if he starts to cross as a vehicle passes by, he will reach the other side before another vehicle gets to that point.

He crosses back with the same procedure. Find the probability that he completes each crossing without another vehicle arriving at his crossing point while he is crossing.

T is distributed exponentially with parameter $\lambda = \frac{1}{100}$.

mean time $= \dfrac{1}{\lambda} = 100$ s.

variance $= \dfrac{1}{\lambda^2} = 10\,000$ s^2.

$F(t) = 1 - e^{-t/100}$.

$P(t > 50) = 1 - P(t \leqslant 50) = e^{-50/100} = e^{-1/2} \approx 0{\cdot}607$.

On the first crossing $P(t > 50) \approx 0{\cdot}607$.

On the second crossing $P(t > 50) \approx 0{\cdot}607$.

$\quad P(t > 50$ on each crossing$) \approx 0{\cdot}607 \times 0{\cdot}607$ (by independence)

$$\approx 0{\cdot}368.$$

Exercise 4.2

1 A police radar trap catches X motorists per hour who are speeding on a certain stretch of motorway. Assuming that X is a Poisson random variable with parameter 6·3, find the probability that the time between successive speeders is less than 15 minutes.

2 Accidents occur at random on a certain road at the rate of 2 per day. Find, to three decimal places, the probability that, after one particular accident has occurred, there will be at least 12 hours before the next accident.

3 Vehicles pass a particular point on a main road at the rate of 120 per hour. Write down the pdf of the time in minutes between 2 consecutive vehicles. A man takes 30 seconds to cross the road. Find the probability that he will be able to complete his crossing between 2 consecutive vehicles.

4 A certain make of electric iron needs repairing on average once every 3 years. Assuming that the times between repairs are exponentially distributed, find the probability that an iron of this make will go on working for at least 4 years without needing a repair.

5 A target contains three concentric circular rings X, Y, and Z of radii 1, 2, and 3 units, respectively. A shot scores 5 points if it falls inside X, 3 between X and Y, 1 between Y and Z, and 0 outside Z. If the probability density function of r, the distance of a shot from the centre, is e^{-r}, find the probability of each possible score, and show that the expected value of the score for a single shot is approximately 3·94.

4.3 The normal distribution

The continuous random variable X whose pdf f(x) is given by

$$f(x) = \frac{1}{\sigma\sqrt{(2\pi)}}\, e^{-(x-\mu)^2/(2\sigma^2)} \text{ for all real } x,$$

where μ and σ are real constants and $\sigma > 0$, has a *normal (or Gaussian) distribution*. We can write this $X \sim N(\mu, \sigma^2)$, to be read as X is normally distributed with parameters μ and σ^2. This distribution is probably the most important of all the theoretical probability distributions, and it serves as a model for data from many fields of study. It was first investigated in the eighteenth century by mathematicians who were studying the distributions of errors when quantities were measured, although its mathematical properties were not fully developed until the work of Gauss in the early nineteenth century. Soon after this, Quetelet, the astronomer, was the first to use a normal distribution in the study of biological quantities, and Galton used it in his work on heredity later in the nineteenth century.

From the pdf we can state some important properties of the distribution.
(i) The curve representing $f(x)$ is symmetrical about the line $x = \mu$.
(ii) x can take all values between $-\infty$ and $+\infty$.
(iii) The x-axis is an asymptote to the curve at both ends.
(iv) The maximum value on the curve is at $x = \mu$, where the ordinate is
$$\frac{1}{\sigma\sqrt{(2\pi)}}.$$

A sketch of the distribution is shown in Fig. 4.3.

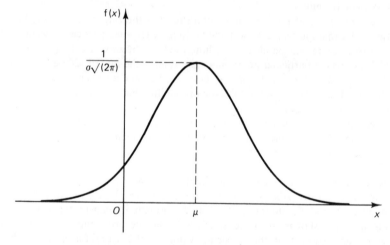

Fig. 4.3

In order to find the mean and variance of this distribution, we use the values of three definite integrals, two of which involve calculus beyond the scope of this text.

(i) $\displaystyle\int_{-\infty}^{+\infty} e^{-t^2/2} \, dt = \sqrt{(2\pi)},$

(ii) $\displaystyle\int_{-\infty}^{+\infty} t e^{-t^2/2}\, dt = \left[-e^{-t^2/2}\right]_{-\infty}^{+\infty} = 0,$

as is otherwise obvious because the integrand is an odd function,

(iii) $\displaystyle\int_{-\infty}^{+\infty} t^2 e^{-t^2/2}\, dt = \sqrt{(2\pi)}.$

Using these results,

$$
\begin{aligned}
E(X) &= \int_{-\infty}^{+\infty} \frac{x}{\sigma\sqrt{(2\pi)}}\, e^{-(x-\mu)^2/(2\sigma^2)}\, dx \\
&= \frac{\sigma}{\sigma\sqrt{(2\pi)}} \int_{-\infty}^{+\infty} (z\sigma + \mu)\, e^{-z^2/2}\, dz, \text{ where } \frac{x-\mu}{\sigma} = z, \\
&= \frac{\sigma}{\sqrt{(2\pi)}} \int_{-\infty}^{+\infty} z e^{-z^2/2}\, dz + \frac{\mu}{\sqrt{(2\pi)}} \int_{-\infty}^{+\infty} e^{-z^2/2}\, dz, \\
&= 0 + \frac{\mu\sqrt{(2\pi)}}{\sqrt{(2\pi)}} = \mu.
\end{aligned}
$$

Thus, the mean is the parameter μ, as is clear from the symmetry of the curve in Fig. 4.3.

$$
\begin{aligned}
E(X^2) &= \int_{-\infty}^{+\infty} \frac{x^2}{\sigma\sqrt{(2\pi)}}\, e^{-(x-\mu)^2/(2\sigma^2)}\, dx \\
&= \frac{\sigma}{\sigma\sqrt{(2\pi)}} \int_{-\infty}^{+\infty} (z\sigma + \mu)^2\, e^{-z^2/2}\, dz, \text{ where } z = \frac{x-\mu}{\sigma}, \\
&= \frac{1}{\sqrt{(2\pi)}} \left[\sigma^2 \int_{-\infty}^{+\infty} z^2 e^{-z^2/2}\, dz + 2\sigma\mu \int_{-\infty}^{+\infty} z e^{-z^2/2}\, dz + \mu^2 \int_{-\infty}^{+\infty} e^{-z^2/2}\, dz \right] \\
&= \frac{1}{\sqrt{(2\pi)}} [\sigma^2\sqrt{(2\pi)} + 0 + \mu^2\sqrt{(2\pi)}] \\
&= \sigma^2 + \mu^2.
\end{aligned}
$$
$\Rightarrow \mathrm{Var}(X) = (\sigma^2 + \mu^2) - \mu^2 = \sigma^2.$

Hence, the variance is the parameter σ^2.

To calculate probabilities associated with $N(\mu,\sigma^2)$, we would need to evaluate the integral of $f(x)$ between the two limits in which we are interested. This is obviously a very difficult task, and so we simplify the problem by *standardising* the variable in order to transform $N(\mu,\sigma^2)$ to the *standard normal distribution* $N(0,1)$. This latter distribution has a mean of zero and a variance of 1; that is, we have transformed the mean to the origin, and, in finding areas under the curve for the probabilities, we can use the symmetric property of the distribution curve.

In Chapter 2, we had the results

$$E(aX + b) = aE(X) + b, \quad \mathrm{Var}(aX + b) = a^2\mathrm{Var}(X).$$

If we make the transformation

$$Z = \frac{X - \mu}{\sigma},$$

then

$$E(Z) = \frac{1}{\sigma} E(X) - \frac{\mu}{\sigma} = \frac{\mu - \mu}{\sigma} = 0,$$

$$\text{Var}(Z) = \frac{1}{\sigma^2} \text{Var}(X) = \frac{\sigma^2}{\sigma^2} = 1.$$

This transformation transforms the mean μ for X to the mean 0 for Z, and variance σ^2 for X to variance 1 for Z, transforming $X \sim N(\mu, \sigma^2)$ into $Z \sim N(0,1)$. Z is called *the standard normal variate*.

The pdf of $N(0,1)$ is usually written as $\phi(z)$ and the distribution function as $\Phi(z)$.

We have

$$\phi(z) = \frac{1}{\sqrt{(2\pi)}} e^{-z^2/2},$$

and

$$P(Z < z) \equiv \Phi(z) = \int_{-\infty}^{z} \phi(z)dz = \int_{-\infty}^{z} \frac{1}{\sqrt{(2\pi)}} e^{-z^2/2} \, dz.$$

This integral cannot be evaluated by elementary calculus, but it can be evaluated numerically, and these numerical evaluations have been tabulated for

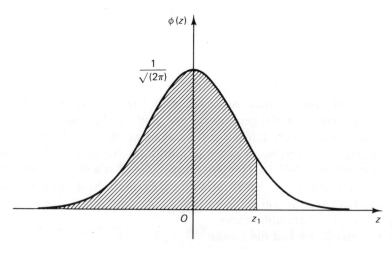

Fig. 4.4

varying values of z. A sketch of $N(0,1)$ is shown in Fig. 4.4, the shaded region representing $\Phi(z_1)$. Since the total area under the curve must be equal to 1 (certainty), the area on each side of the line $z = 0$ must equal 0·5 by symmetry. The tables of values connecting z and $\Phi(z)$ are given, principally, in three different forms.

Some tables show corresponding values of z and $\Phi(z)$; that is, they give values of the shaded area in Fig. 4.4 and the corresponding z-values. Of this type of table, some show both negative and positive values of z. Others show only positive values of z and expect us to use the symmetry of the curve and the fact that the total area under the curve is 1, to deduce the corresponding value of $\Phi(z)$ for $z < 0$. For example, to find the shaded area in Fig. 4.5, we need to find $\Phi(-z_1)$. By symmetry, this area is equal to the area from $z = z_1$ to $z = +\infty$. Hence,

$$\Phi(-z_1) = 1 - \Phi(z_1).$$

We can use this equation and the value of $\Phi(z_1)$ for the corresponding positive value of z_1 in order to find $\Phi(-z_1)$.

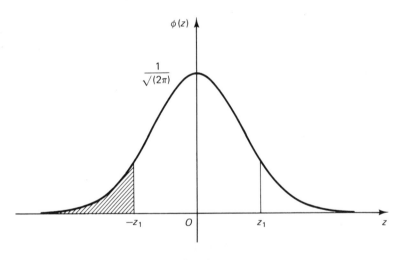

Fig. 4.5

A second form of table gives the area under the curve for the interval $(z,+\infty)$, and this means, as we can see from Fig. 4.4, that the table is showing us corresponding values of z and $1 - \Phi(z)$.

A third form of table gives the area under the curve from $z = 0$ to $z = z_1$, the shaded region of Fig. 4.6, and, hence, shows corresponding values of z_1 and $[\Phi(z_1) - 0·5]$. Any other associated area can then be obtained by symmetry.

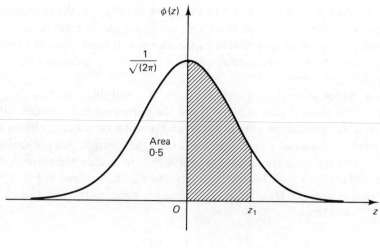

Fig. 4.6

Although this availability of different types of table may seem confusing, this is not really so, as all tables are clearly marked in words, or a diagram shows the area values which are given by the table corresponding to each z. In problem solving, we soon become used to using one particular type of table. For the solved problems in this text, a table showing $\Phi(z)$ for corresponding positive z values has been used (Table 4.1).

Table 4.1   The distribution function, $\Phi(z)$, of the normal probability function, $\phi(z)$

$$\phi(z) = \frac{1}{\sqrt{(2\pi)}}\ e^{-z^2/2},\ \Phi(z) = \int_{-\infty}^{z} \phi(t)\ dt.$$

Table 4.1 (*continued*)

z	·00	·01	·02	·03	·04	·05	·06	·07	·08	·09
0·0	·5000	·5040	·5080	·5120	·5160	·5199	·5239	·5279	·5319	·5359
0·1	·5398	·5438	·5478	·5517	·5557	·5596	·5636	·5675	·5714	·5753
0·2	·5793	·5832	·5871	·5910	·5948	·5987	·6026	·6064	·6103	·6141
0·3	·6179	·6217	·6255	·6293	·6331	·6368	·6406	·6443	·6480	·6517
0·4	·6554	·6591	·6628	·6664	·6700	·6736	·6772	·6808	·6844	·6879
0·5	·6915	·6950	·6985	·7019	·7054	·7088	·7123	·7157	·7190	·7224
0·6	·7257	·7291	·7324	·7357	·7389	·7422	·7454	·7486	·7517	·7549
0·7	·7580	·7611	·7642	·7673	·7704	·7734	·7764	·7794	·7823	·7852
0·8	·7881	·7910	·7939	·7967	·7995	·8023	·8051	·8078	·8106	·8133
0·9	·8159	·8186	·8212	·8238	·8264	·8289	·8315	·8340	·8365	·8389
1·0	·8413	·8438	·8461	·8485	·8508	·8531	·8554	·8577	·8599	·8621
1·1	·8643	·8665	·8686	·8708	·8729	·8749	·8770	·8790	·8810	·8830
1·2	·8849	·8869	·8888	·8907	·8925	·8944	·8962	·8980	·8997	·9015
1·3	·9032	·9049	·9066	·9082	·9099	·9115	·9131	·9147	·9162	·9177
1·4	·9192	·9207	·9222	·9236	·9251	·9265	·9279	·9292	·9306	·9319
1·5	·9332	·9345	·9357	·9370	·9382	·9394	·9406	·9418	·9429	·9441
1·6	·9452	·9463	·9474	·9484	·9495	·9505	·9515	·9525	·9535	·9545
1·7	·9554	·9564	·9573	·9582	·9591	·9599	·9608	·9616	·9625	·9633
1·8	·9641	·9649	·9656	·9664	·9671	·9678	·9686	·9693	·9699	·9706
1·9	·9713	·9719	·9726	·9732	·9738	·9744	·9750	·9756	·9761	·9767
2·0	·97725	·97778	·97831	·97882	·97932	·97982	·98030	·98077	·98124	·98169
2·1	·98214	·98257	·98300	·98341	·98382	·98422	·98461	·98500	·98537	·98574
2·2	·98610	·98645	·98679	·98713	·98745	·98778	·98809	·98840	·98870	·98899
2·3	·98928	·98956	·98983	·99010	·99036	·99061	·99086	·99111	·99134	·99158
2·4	·99180	·99202	·99224	·99245	·99266	·99286	·99305	·99324	·99343	·99361
2·5	·99379	·99396	·99413	·99430	·99446	·99461	·99477	·99492	·99506	·99520
2·6	·99534	·99547	·99560	·99573	·99585	·99598	·99609	·99621	·99632	·99643
2·7	·99653	·99664	·99674	·99683	·99693	·99702	·99711	·99720	·99728	·99736
2·8	·99744	·99752	·99760	·99767	·99774	·99781	·99788	·99795	·99801	·99807
2·9	·99813	·99819	·99825	·99831	·99836	·99841	·99846	·99851	·99856	·99861
3·0	·99865	·99869	·99874	·99878	·99882	·99886	·99889	·99893	·99896	·99900

z	3·1	3·2	3·3	3·4	3·5	3·6	3·7	3·8	3·9	4·0
Φ	·99903	·99931	·99952	·99966	·99977	·99984	·99989	·99993	·99995	·99997

Sometimes it is necessary to interpolate linearly for a value of z which lies between given values of z in the table, just as we would interpolate when using other tables such as sine or cosine tables.

You will notice that, in all three types of table mentioned, there is a definite base from which the integral is evaluated, $-\infty$, $+\infty$, and 0, respectively. Should we wish to find the probability that z lies between z_1 and z_2, we must take the areas from whichever base is used in the particular table with which we are working, and add or subtract areas as necessary.

When a problem is being worked, a diagram is extremely helpful, not only because we may need to obtain areas other than those given directly by the table, but also so that we can really understand the problem and locate the area that we need. For example, the shaded area in Fig. 4.7 represents

$$P(z_1 \leqslant z \leqslant z_2) = \Phi(z_2) - \Phi(z_1).$$

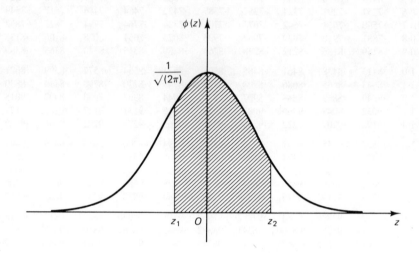

Fig. 4.7

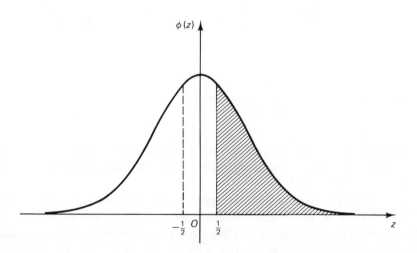

Fig. 4.8

Example 7 Find $P(X \geqslant 0)$ when X is distributed
(a) $N(-3,36)$ — that is, with mean -3, variance 36,
(b) $N(3,36)$.

(a) Transforming, we have

$$Z = \frac{X - \mu}{\sigma} = \frac{0 - (-3)}{6} = \frac{1}{2},$$

since $\mu = -3$, $\sigma^2 = 36$. $X \geqslant 0$ corresponds to $Z \geqslant \frac{1}{2}$, where $Z \sim N(0,1)$. We require the shaded area shown in Fig. 4.8 — that is,

$$P(Z \geqslant \tfrac{1}{2}) = 1 - \Phi(\tfrac{1}{2}) = 1 - 0\cdot6915 = 0\cdot308(5).$$

(b) $Z = \dfrac{0 - 3}{6} = -\dfrac{1}{2}$ and $X \geqslant 0$ corresponds to $Z \geqslant -\frac{1}{2}$, where $Z \sim N(0,1)$. We require the area under the curve from $z = -\frac{1}{2}$ to $z = +\infty$ in Fig. 4.8. By symmetry, this is equal to the area from $z = -\infty$ to $z = +\frac{1}{2}$, which is $\Phi(\tfrac{1}{2})$

$$\Rightarrow P(X \geqslant 0) = P(Z \geqslant -\tfrac{1}{2}) = \Phi(\tfrac{1}{2}) = 0\cdot691(5).$$

Example 8 Given that the IQ scores of young people between 15 and 17 years of age are distributed $N(100,169)$, find the proportion of this age group who have IQs (a) above 110, (b) below 75, (c) above 80, (d) between 75 and 80, (e) between 110 and 140, (f) between 80 and 110.

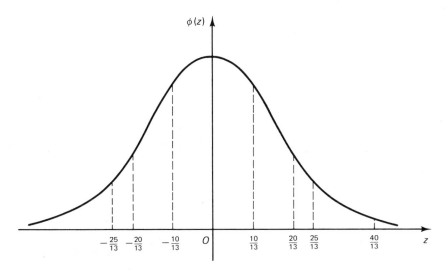

Fig. 4.9

$\mu = 100$, $\sigma^2 = 169$, $\Rightarrow \sigma = 13$.

$$Z = \frac{X - \mu}{\sigma} = \frac{X - 100}{13} \text{ and } Z \sim N(0,1).$$

(a) $X > 110$ corresponds to $Z > \dfrac{10}{13}$. (See Fig. 4.9.)

$$P(X > 110) = P\left(Z > \frac{10}{13}\right) = 1 - \Phi\left(\frac{10}{13}\right) = 1 - 0\cdot7791 \approx 0\cdot221.$$

(b) $X < 75$ corresponds to $Z < -\dfrac{25}{13}$.

$$P(X < 75) = P\left(Z < -\frac{25}{13}\right) = 1 - \Phi\left(\frac{25}{13}\right), \text{ by symmetry,}$$

$$\approx 1 - 0\cdot9728 \approx 0\cdot027.$$

(c) $X > 80$ corresponds to $Z > -\dfrac{20}{13}$.

$$P(X > 80) = P\left(Z > -\frac{20}{13}\right) = \Phi\left(\frac{20}{13}\right) \approx 0\cdot938.$$

(d) $75 < X < 80$ corresponds to $-\dfrac{25}{13} < Z < -\dfrac{20}{13}$.

$$P(75 < X < 80) = P\left(-\frac{25}{13} < Z < -\frac{20}{13}\right)$$

$$= \Phi\left(\frac{25}{13}\right) - \Phi\left(\frac{20}{13}\right), \text{ by symmetry,}$$

$$= 0\cdot9728 - 0\cdot9380 \approx 0\cdot035.$$

(e) $110 < X < 140$ corresponds to $\dfrac{10}{13} < Z < \dfrac{40}{13}$.

$$P(110 < X < 140) = P\left(\frac{10}{13} < Z < \frac{40}{13}\right) = \Phi\left(\frac{40}{13}\right) - \Phi\left(\frac{10}{13}\right)$$

$$= 0\cdot9990 - 0\cdot7791 \approx 0\cdot22.$$

(f) $80 < X < 110$ corresponds to $-\dfrac{20}{13} < Z < \dfrac{10}{13}$.

$$P(80 < X < 110) = P\left(-\frac{20}{13} < Z < \frac{10}{13}\right) = \Phi\left(\frac{10}{13}\right) - \Phi\left(-\frac{20}{13}\right)$$

$$= \Phi\left(\frac{10}{13}\right) - \left[1 - \Phi\left(\frac{20}{13}\right)\right]$$

$$= \Phi\left(\frac{10}{13}\right) + \Phi\left(\frac{20}{13}\right) - 1$$

$$\approx 0\cdot717.$$

Example 9 The dry weight of a certain bedding plant is a normal variable with mean 7 g and standard deviation 1·5 g. Find the dry weight which is exceeded by 25% of these bedding plants. Find also the range of values, symmetric about the mean, which includes 98% of the dry weights of all the plants.

$$X \sim N(7,(1\cdot5)^2) \qquad Z = \frac{X - \mu}{\sigma} = \frac{X - 7}{1\cdot5}, \text{ where } Z \sim N(0,1).$$

We want to find the value of Z such that the shaded area of Fig. 4.10 equals 0·25, and, hence, $\Phi(z) = 0\cdot75$. Using the tables so that we are looking up the value of z for a given $\Phi(z)$, we find $Z = 0\cdot674$ when $\Phi(Z) = 0\cdot75$

$$\Rightarrow \frac{X - 7}{1\cdot5} = 0\cdot674 \Rightarrow X = 8\cdot011.$$

The dry weight which is exceeded by 25% of the plants is 8·01 g.

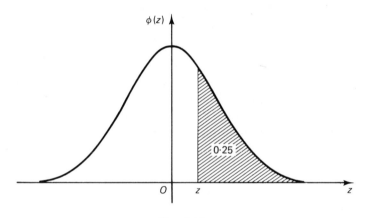

Fig. 4.10

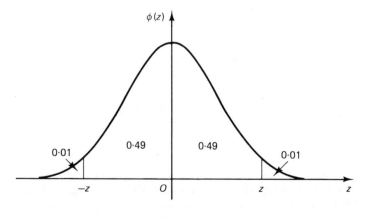

Fig. 4.11

For the symmetric interval which includes 98% of all the dry weights, we see in Fig. 4.11 that we need

$$\Phi(Z) = 0{\cdot}5 + 0{\cdot}49 = 0{\cdot}99$$
$$\Rightarrow Z = 2{\cdot}327$$
$$\Rightarrow \frac{X - 7}{1{\cdot}5} = 2{\cdot}327 \Rightarrow X = 7 \pm 3{\cdot}49 = (3{\cdot}51,\ 10{\cdot}49).$$

The range within which 98% of the dry weights lie is 3·51 to 10·49 g.

Example 10 Find the probability that a normally distributed random variable X differs from its mean by less than twice its standard deviation.

Let $X \sim N(\mu, \sigma^2)$, $Z = \dfrac{X - \mu}{\sigma}$, where $Z \sim N(0,1)$.

$\mu - 2\sigma < X < \mu + 2\sigma$ corresponds to $-2 < Z < 2$.
$$\begin{aligned}
P(-2 < Z < 2) &= \Phi(2) - \Phi(-2) \\
&= \Phi(2) - 1 + \Phi(2) \\
&= 2\Phi(2) - 1 = 2 \times 0{\cdot}977\,25 - 1 = 0{\cdot}9545.
\end{aligned}$$

This result is sometimes called the '2-σ Rule'; that is, that approximately 95% of the distribution lies within a distance of 2σ either side of the mean μ, where σ is the standard deviation of the distribution. In fact, $1{\cdot}96\sigma$ either side of μ gives a better approximation for the 95% interval, but '2-σ' is a useful rule to use.

The normal distribution used as an approximation to the binomial distribution B(*n,p*)

For the binomial distribution with $p = \frac{1}{2}$, the sketch of the probability function is symmetrical and, if n is large, so that there is a large number of points plotted on the sketch, the graph has the characteristic shape of the normal distribution, although in B(n,p) the variable is discrete. Obviously, the larger n becomes, and the nearer p is to $\frac{1}{2}$, the more closely will the sketch of B(n,p) approach a normal distribution shape.

It can be proved mathematically that, if $X \sim B(n,p)$, then for large n and p not too close to 0 or 1, the distribution of X may be approximated by N(np,npq), where $q = 1 - p$. That is, B(n,p) can be approximated by a normal distribution with mean np and variance npq. A common rule of thumb for the conditions on n and p, is to use the approximation only when np and nq both exceed 5.

However, when we make this approximation, we are approximating a discrete variable by a continuous one, and so we make a *continuity correction*. This means that we must take particular care when deciding on the end-points of the intervals involved. To do this, we consider each discrete point as representing a corresponding continuous range. For example, the integers 2 and 5 would be considered as the corresponding ranges $1\frac{1}{2}-2\frac{1}{2}$ and $4\frac{1}{2}-5\frac{1}{2}$, respectively. Then, if we wished to find $P(X \le 2)$, we would use $P(X < 2\cdot5)$, and $P(X = 5)$ would be $P(4\cdot5 < X < 5\cdot5)$, in the approximate normal distribution.

Example 11 Calculate $P(X = 2)$ when $X \sim B(14,0\cdot4)$
(a) exactly,
(b) using a normal approximation.

(a) $P(X = 2) = \binom{14}{2}(0\cdot6)^{12}(0\cdot4)^2 = 91(0\cdot6)^{12}(0\cdot4)^2 \approx 0\cdot0317.$

(b) Since $np = 14(0\cdot4)$ and $npq = 14(0\cdot4)(0\cdot6)$, then $1\cdot5 < X < 2\cdot5$ corresponds to

$$\frac{1\cdot5 - 5\cdot6}{\sqrt{(3\cdot36)}} < Z < \frac{2\cdot5 - 5\cdot6}{\sqrt{(3\cdot36)}}$$
$$\Rightarrow -2\cdot2367 < Z < -1\cdot6912.$$
$$P(-2\cdot2367 < Z < -1\cdot6912) = \Phi(2\cdot2367) - \Phi(1\cdot6912)$$
$$= 0\cdot9873 - 0\cdot9546 \approx 0\cdot0327.$$
$$\Rightarrow P(X = 2) \approx 0\cdot0327.$$

We can see that the error in the approximation is quite small, approximately 3%, even though n is not very large.

Example 12 There is a probability of $0\cdot75$ that, when a fly is sprayed with a certain fly-killer, it will die. Given that 6 flies are sprayed, find the probability that at least 5 of them will die.

A swarm of 100 flies is sprayed. Estimate the probability that at least 70 of them will be killed by the spray.

Here we have a binomial distribution $B(n,0\cdot75)$ for X, the number of flies killed.
For $n = 6$, $P(X \ge 5) = P(5) + P(6) = 6(0\cdot25)(0\cdot75)^5 + (0\cdot75)^6$
$$= 2\cdot25(0\cdot75)^5$$
$$= 0\cdot534.$$

For $n = 100$, we will use the normal approximation $N(75,18\cdot75)$, and make a continuity correction.
$$X > 69\cdot5 \text{ corresponds to } Z > \frac{69\cdot5 - 75}{\sqrt{18\cdot75}} = -1\cdot2702.$$
$$P(Z > -1\cdot2702) = \Phi(1\cdot2702) \text{ by symmetry,}$$
$$= 0\cdot898.$$
$$P(>70 \text{ flies killed}) \approx 0\cdot898.$$

Here a great deal of arithmetic would have been required to calculate the probability from $B(100,0\cdot75)$.

Example 13   A machine produces articles of which, on average, 20% are defective. Find an approximate value for the probability that a random sample of 400 of the articles will contain more than 96 which are defective.

$$p = 0.2, \quad q = 1 - p = 0.8, \quad n = 400 \quad \Rightarrow X \sim B(400, 0.2).$$

We use the approximation N(80, 64), and a continuity correction. $X > 96$ corresponds to $Z > \dfrac{96.5 - 80}{8} = 2.0625.$

$P(Z > 2.0625) = 1 - \Phi(2.0625) = 1 - 0.9804 = 0.0196 \sim 0.02.$

The normal distribution used as an approximation to the Poisson distribution

The Poisson distribution with mean and variance μ, can be approximated, for large values of μ, by $N(\mu, \mu)$. The usual rule is to interpret 'large values' as meaning $\mu > 20$, although the approximation is quite good for $\mu > 10$. The larger μ becomes, the better is the approximation. We are again approximating a discrete random variable by a continuous one, and, as we did when approximating the binomial by a normal distribution, we make a *continuity correction* in the same way.

Example 14   The number of deaths in road accidents in Greater London in a given month can be assumed to have a Poisson distribution with mean 22. Calculate approximate values for the probabilities that there will be next month
(a) less than 20 road deaths,
(b) 25 or more road deaths.

Since $\mu = 22$ we will use the approximation N(22, 22) and a continuity correction.

(a) $X < 19.5$ corresponds to $Z < \dfrac{19.5 - 22}{\sqrt{22}} = -0.5330.$

$\qquad P(Z < -0.5330) = \Phi(-0.5330) = 1 - \Phi(0.5330) = 0.297$
$\qquad\qquad\qquad\qquad \Rightarrow P(<20 \text{ deaths}) \approx 0.297.$

(b) $X > 24.5$ corresponds to $Z > \dfrac{24.5 - 22}{\sqrt{22}} = 0.5330.$

$\qquad P(Z > 0.5330) = 1 - \Phi(0.5330) = 0.297$
$\qquad\qquad\qquad\qquad \Rightarrow P(25 \text{ or more deaths}) \approx 0.297.$

Example 15   At an emergency centre, '999' calls come in at an average rate of 3 per hour. Find the probability that there are 5 or more calls in a 2 hour period. Estimate the probability that there are 30 or more calls in a 12 hour period.

The conditions given in the question indicate that it is reasonable to assume that the number of calls in an interval of time h hours is a Poisson variable with mean $\mu = 3h$.

For $h = 2$, $\mu = 6$.

$$P(X_2 \geqslant 5) = 1 - P(0) - P(1) - P(2) - P(3) - P(4)$$
$$= 1 - e^{-6}\left(1 + 6 + \frac{6^2}{2} + \frac{6^3}{6} + \frac{6^4}{24}\right)$$
$$= 1 - 115e^{-6} = 0 \cdot 715.$$

For $h = 12$, $\mu = 36$.

We use the approximation $N(36,36)$, and a continuity correction.

$$P(X_{12} > 29 \cdot 5) = P\left(Z > \frac{29 \cdot 5 - 36}{6}\right) = P\left(Z > \frac{-6 \cdot 5}{6}\right)$$
$$= P(Z > -1 \cdot 0833)$$
$$= \Phi(1 \cdot 0833), \text{ by symmetry,}$$
$$= 0 \cdot 8607$$
$$\Rightarrow P(30 \text{ or more calls in 12 hours}) \approx 0 \cdot 861.$$

Exercise 4.3

1 Given that X has distribution $N(2, 0 \cdot 16)$, evaluate
   (a) $P(X \geqslant 2 \cdot 3)$,
   (b) $P(1 \cdot 8 \leqslant X \leqslant 2 \cdot 1)$.

2 The diameter of a certain type of copper tubing is normally distributed with mean 8 mm and variance $0 \cdot 04$ mm^2. Find the probability that a diameter will exceed $8 \cdot 1$ mm. A piece of this tubing is rejected if the diameter differs from the mean diameter by more than $0 \cdot 25$ mm. Find the probability that a piece of the tubing will be rejected.

3 A large cargo of tomatoes has, on average, 1 bad tomato in 10. Find, to two significant figures, the probability that a random sample of 100 will contain 15 or more bad tomatoes.

4 A machine produces articles of which, on average, 5% are defective. Use a suitable normal approximation to calculate, to three decimal places, the probability that, in a random sample of 800 articles, more than 45 will prove to be defective.

5 A telephone exchange receives calls at random at an average rate of 120 calls every hour. Use the normal approximation to the Poisson distribution to calculate the probability that fewer than 120 calls, but not fewer than 90 calls, are received in a 1 hour period.

6 Bungs are manufactured which are to fit holes in barrels. The diameter X of the bungs is normally distributed with mean 48 mm and standard deviation $0 \cdot 3$ mm. The diameter Y of the holes is normally distributed with mean 49 mm and standard deviation $0 \cdot 5$ mm.
   (a) Find the proportion of bungs with diameter greater than $48 \cdot 5$ mm.
   (b) Find the proportion of holes with diameter less than $48 \cdot 5$ mm.
   (c) If the bungs and holes are selected at random, find the proportion of bungs that will be too big for the holes.

Miscellaneous Exercise 4

1   The probability that a fluorescent light-tube lasts longer than t hours is $e^{-t/k}$. Find the probability density function for the lifetime of a tube and state the mean lifetime.

    Given that the mean lifetime is 2000 hours, find the probability that a tube will last more than 3500 hours. If the manufacturer wishes to ensure that fewer than 1 in 1500 of his tubes fail before 10 hours of life, find the smallest mean lifetime which he can allow his tubes to have.

2   A certain continuous value is recorded, to the nearest whole number, as 5. Given that the exact value has a uniform distribution, find the probability that the exact value is (a) between 4·8 and 5·1, (b) greater than 4·9, (c) less than 4·7.

3   The mass printed on a packet of sultanas by the manufacturer is 500 g. In fact, it is discovered that the packets coming from the factory have a mean mass of 505 g and a standard deviation of 2·5 g. Assuming that the masses are normally distributed, estimate the percentage of packets weighing between 500·5 g and 510·5 g. If the manufacturer decides to alter the mean mass so that 10% of the output is less than the intended mass of 500 g, find the new mean, assuming that the standard deviation remains unaltered.

4   A tyre manufacturer guarantees to replace his tyres free if they fail within 1 year of purchase and to replace them at half-price if they fail in more than 1 year but less than 2 years. Replacement tyres are not replaced if they fail. From his experience of production over the years, the manufacturer knows that the time to failure has had a normal distribution with mean of 3·5 years and a standard deviation of 0·9 years. Calculate the probability that
(a) a tyre will fail in under 1 year,
(b) a tyre will fail in more than 1 year but under 2 years.
The manufacturer sells a new tyre for £35, of which £25 is the cost of production. Calculate his expected profit from the sale of 1000 tyres.

5   In a large café 1 in 3 of the customers buys a cup of tea.
(a) Find the probability that at least 4 out of the first 9 customers will buy a cup of tea.
(b) Given that the probability that 1000 customers will buy fewer than k cups of tea is 0·98, find k.
Given that overall 2 customers per 1000 make a complaint and assuming that complaints occur independently, find the probability of receiving fewer than 2 complaints from 200 customers.

6   The probability density function f(t) of the time T to failure of an item is given by

$$f(t) = \frac{1}{k} e^{-t/k} \ (0 < t < \infty).$$

Find the mean time to failure and the variance.

    Two components in an engine have failure time distributions corresponding to means k and $3k$, respectively. The engine will stop if either component fails, and the failures of the two components are independent. Show that the chance of the engine continuing to work for a time k from the start is approximately 0·26.

7   Electric bulbs have an average life of 3000 hours and 98% of the bulbs have a life of at least 2500 hours. Estimate, to two decimal places, the standard deviation, stating any assumption you are making about the distribution.

    Find the percentage of the bulbs which would be expected

(a) to last more than 3300 hours,

(b) to fail in less than 2400 hours.

8 The natural logarithm of the emerald content in carats of a cubic metre of a certain limestone is a normal variable with mean 1·69 and variance 0·212. Find the probability that a cubic metre of the limestone will contain

(a) less than 1·41 carats,

(b) between 1·41 and 2·84 carats.

9 The time T seconds between the arrival of successive vehicles at a point on a road has pdf f(t) given by f$(t) = \lambda e^{-t/a}$, for t $\geqslant$ 0, where λ and a are positive constants. Find λ in terms of a and sketch the graph of the probability density function.

Given that $a = 50$, state the mean and variance.

A pedestrian takes 30 seconds to cross the road at this point. With $a = 50$, calculate the probability that, if she sets off as one vehicle passes, she will complete the crossing before the next vehicle arrives. Calculate also the probability that, if she adopts the same procedure on the return journey, she completes each crossing without a vehicle arriving while she is in the process of crossing.

10 An athlete finds that, in throwing the discus, his distances form a normal distribution with mean 55 m and standard deviation 4·3 m. Calculate the probability that he will throw the discus more than 61 m on a given occasion.

Find the probability that 3 independent throws will all be less than 61 m.

Find the distance that he can expect to exceed once in 100 throws.

11 A man leaves home at 07.30 every morning in order to arrive at work at 09.00. Over a long period, he finds that he is late once in 20 times. He then tries leaving home at 07.20 and finds that over a similar period he is late once in 50 times. Given that the time of his journey has a normal distribution, find the latest time at which he should leave home in order not to be late more than once in 100 times.

12 Given that the probability of a male birth is 0·517, find, to three decimal places, the probability that there will be fewer boys than girls in 1000 births. Find, to the nearest hundred, the size of the smallest sample which should be taken so that the probability of fewer boys than girls is less than 0·03. (Assume here that the sample size is large enough to make a continuity correction unnecessary.)

13 Axles are made of nominal length 1 m but in fact they form a normal distribution with mean 1·01 m and standard deviation 0·01 m. Each axle costs £5 to make and may be used immediately if its length lies between 0·99 m and 1·02 m. If its length is less than 0·99 m, the axle is useless but has a scrap value of £1. If its length exceeds 1·02 m, it may be shortened and used at an extra cost of £1·50. Find the cost per usable axle.

14 In the assembly of an engine, a cylindrical rod with circular cross-section of diameter a has to fit into a circular collar of diameter A. Measurement of a large number of these rods and collars indicates that both a and A are normally distributed about respective means 10·02 cm and 10·17 cm with respective standard deviations 0·04 cm and 0·06 cm. If components are selected at random for assembly, find the percentage of the rods which are likely to be too big for the collars for which they are chosen.

15 The heights of boys aged 13–14 years are normally distributed with mean 162 cm and standard deviation 6 cm. The heights of girls in the same age range are normally distributed with mean 158 cm and standard deviation 5 cm. Determine, to three decimal places, the probabilities of differences in height greater than 4 cm between

(a) 2 boys in the group,

(b) 2 girls in the group.

(c) a boy and a girl in the group.

16 The lifetime, T hours, of a transistor is assumed to follow the exponential distribution with probability density function $f(t) = \lambda e^{-\lambda t}$ ($\lambda > 0, t > 0$). Find the mean lifetime of a transistor and show that the probability of its surviving this length of time or longer is approximately 0.368.

Given that the mean life is 2500 hours, find the number of hours for which the manufacturer should guarantee his transistors if he wants 98% of his output to satisfy his guarantee.

17 Show that the variance of the uniform distribution of a variable which lies at random between $-k$ and $+k$ is $k^2/3$.

The weights of N passengers in an aircraft are to be totalled but before they are added, each weight is rounded off to the nearest 1 kg thus introducing an error which has a uniform distribution. Find the mean and variance of the total error of the sum.

Assuming that, when N is large, the total error has a normal distribution, find the greatest value of N for which the probability that the total rounding off error lies outside the limits ± 10 kg is less than 0.01.

18 The weights of the males of a type of goldfish are normally distributed with mean 30 g and variance 9 g^2. The weights of the females are distributed N(25,4). Sketch the distribution of

(a) the weights of a population of half male and half female goldfish,

(b) the total weight of a pair of breeding goldfish.

Find the probability that a fish drawn at random from population (a) will have a weight less than 25 g, and also the probability that the total weight of a pair drawn from population (b) will be less than 50 g.

State any assumption which you have made.

19 The probability density function f(t) of the length of life, T hours, of a make of television tube is given by

$$f(t) = ke^{-kt}, t \geqslant 0.$$

Find the probability that a tube will last for T_1 hours more, given that it has already lasted for T_0 hours without failing.

A certain shop has 3 similar television sets containing this make of tube working on display in the window. Find, in terms of T_0 and k, the probability that, owing to failure of the tube, exactly 1 set will fail in the first T_0 hours, another will fail in the next $2T_0$ hours, and the third will last for more than $3T_0$ hours.

ANSWERS

Exercise 1.1

1 $\frac{2}{7}; \frac{1}{7}$

2 (a) $\frac{4}{7}$, (b) $\frac{3}{7}$, (c) $\frac{4}{7}$, (d) $\frac{3}{7}$,
(e) $\frac{3}{7}$

3 (a) $\frac{1}{4}$, (b) $\frac{37}{60}$, (c) $\frac{1}{20}$

4 (a) $\frac{11}{57}$, (b) $\frac{271}{285}$

Exercise 1.2

1 $\frac{4}{7}$

2 (a) $\frac{44}{95}$, (b) $\frac{28}{95}$

3 (a) $\frac{3}{5}$, (b) $\frac{2}{5}$, (c) $\frac{19}{30}$, (d) $\frac{11}{20}$

4 (a) $\frac{3}{4}$, (b) 10, (c) $\frac{3}{5}$

Exercise 1.3

1 $\frac{43}{90}$

2 $\frac{20}{41}$

3 (a) 0·025, (b) 0·4

4 $\frac{1}{15}; \frac{2}{15}$

Exercise 1.4

1 (a) $\frac{19}{32}$, (b) $\frac{77}{128}$

2 $\begin{pmatrix} 0·3 & 0·7 \\ 0·4 & 0·6 \end{pmatrix}; \frac{4}{11}$

Miscellaneous Exercise 1

1 $\frac{7}{15}$

2 (a) $\frac{77}{100}$, (b) $\frac{23}{100}$, (c) $\frac{379}{1800}$

3 0·823

4 $\frac{3}{8}; \frac{1}{4}; \frac{1}{8}$

5 (a) $\frac{3}{44}$, (b) $\frac{3}{11}$, (c) $\frac{29}{44}$

7 0·018

9 (a) 0·105, (b) 0·174, (c) 0·278,
(d) size 2

10 0·09

11 0·52

12 $\frac{5}{18}; \frac{1}{3}; \frac{7}{18}$

13 $\frac{1}{5}; \frac{1}{5}; \frac{2}{5}$

14 (a) $\frac{1}{20}$, (b) $\frac{3}{20}$

15 $\frac{13}{136}$

16 (a) $\frac{1}{3}$, (b) $\frac{2}{3}$

17 (a) $\frac{3}{16}$, (b) 5, (c) 3

18 (a) $\frac{23}{108}$, (b) $\frac{125}{216}$, (c) $\frac{1}{2}; \frac{75}{216}$

Exercise 2.2

1 (a) 3·83; 2·81, (b) 0·3; 9·21

3 £5200

4 $\frac{1}{2}$p

5 1·875

Exercise 2.3

1 $\frac{1}{4}; \frac{7}{32}$

2 $\frac{7}{24}; \frac{41}{30}; \frac{377}{720}$

3 $F(x) = 0$ for $x \leqslant 0$,
$$= \frac{x^2}{4} \text{ for } 0 < x \leqslant 1,$$
$$= \frac{(2x-1)}{4} \text{ for } 1 < x \leqslant 2,$$
$$= \frac{-(x^2 - 6x + 5)}{4}$$
$$\text{for } 2 < x < 3,$$
$$= 1 \text{ for } x \geqslant 3.$$

4 (a) $\frac{1}{4}$, (b) $\frac{8}{x^3}$ for $x > 2$,
0 elsewhere.

5 (a) $\frac{5}{32}$, (b) $\frac{81}{256}$, (c) $\frac{35}{128}$

Miscellaneous Exercise 2

2 $\frac{2^N}{(2^{N+1} - 1)}; 1 - 2k + \left(\frac{k}{2^{n-1}} \right)$

3 $\frac{1}{27}; 5·07; 3·62$; (a) 5·15; 14·50,
(b) 5·07; 148·59

4 3·92, 5·58; 16·58, 139·41

5 2; $\frac{2}{3}$

6 (a) 12, (c) $\frac{3}{5}; \frac{1}{25}$, (d) $\frac{1}{9}$

7 (a) $\frac{1}{2}$, (b) $\dfrac{(1 - \cos 2)}{2}$, (c) $\left(\dfrac{\pi^2}{4} - 2\right)$

8 $\frac{6}{7}; \frac{4}{7}; \frac{4}{21}$

9 $\dfrac{(k+1)}{(k+2)}$

10 $\frac{1}{24}; \frac{5}{8}$

11 $\frac{3}{16}, 4; \frac{19}{80}$

12 $\frac{3}{4}; \frac{4}{5}; \frac{4}{25}$

13 $\frac{1}{18}; \frac{83}{27}; 0.792; 2.59$

14 $\dfrac{\pi}{8}; 2$

15 0.54 hundred litres

16 $\dfrac{2l^2}{3}$

Exercise 3.2

1 $\dfrac{(k-1)}{2}$

2 Loss of $\frac{1}{2}$p

3 4; 8

Exercise 3.3

1 (a) 0.24, (b) 0.63
2 0.75
3 0.384; yes
4 0.337
5 (a) 0.0083, (b) 0.1935

Exercise 3.4

3 (a) $\frac{1}{16}$, (b) $\frac{1}{16}; 2^{-17}$
4 0.019

Exercise 3.5

1 0.143
2 0.097, 0.226, 0.264, 0.205, 0.120, 0.056; 2
3 0.849
4 0.463; 0.558
5 (a) 0.018, (b) 0.433; $P \approx 0.08 \Rightarrow$ yes
6 (a) 0.040, (b) 0.045
7 17

Miscellaneous Exercise 3

1 0.579
2 0.212
3 (a) 0.056, (b) 0.19; 0.53
4 (a) 0.262, (b) 0.371

5 (b) $613/(5^9)$
6 $0.180; £3; 20; 29$
7 $1, 0.95; 0.494; 27.547 \approx 28$
9 $0.9197; 0.00004$
10 (a) 0.444, (b) 0.392, (c) 0.165
11 $P(X = r) = \dfrac{2^{r-1}}{3^r}$ for $r \geq 1$;

$P(Y = r) = \frac{1}{3}$ for $r = 1, 2, 3$

(a) $\frac{8}{27}$, (b) $\frac{38}{81}$

12 (a) 0.995, (b) 0.857
13 0.998
14 (a) 0.665, (b) 0.737, (c) 0.015; $\dfrac{5^{k-1}}{6^k}; 6; 6; 30$

15 (a) 0.8607, (b) 0.0005; 0.8614

Exercise 4.1

1 $\frac{1}{2}$; $F(x) = 0$ for $x < 0$,

$\quad = \dfrac{x}{8}$ for $0 \leq x \leq 8$

$\quad = 1$ for $x > 8$

2 $\frac{1}{2}; 3; \frac{1}{3}$; $F(x) = 0$ for $x < 2$,

$\quad = \dfrac{(x-2)}{2}$ for $2 \leq x \leq 4$,

$\quad = 1$ for $x > 4$

3 $\frac{1}{4}$; $F(x) = 0$ for $x < 0$,

$\quad = \dfrac{x}{4}$ for $0 \leq x \leq 4$,

$\quad = 1$ for $x > 4$; $\frac{3}{4}$

Exercise 4.2

1 0.793
2 0.368
3 $2e^{-2x}$ for $x \geq 0$; $e^{-1} \approx 0.368$
4 0.264
5 $1 - e^{-1}; e^{-1} - e^{-2}; e^{-2} - e^{-3}$

Exercise 4.3

1 (a) 0.2266, (b) 0.2902
2 0.3085; 0.2112
3 0.067
4 0.186
5 0.479
6 (a) 4.78%, (b) 15.87%, (c) 4.32%,

Miscellaneous Exercise 4

1 $\dfrac{e^{-t/k}}{k}$; k hours; 0.174; 14 995 hours

2 (a) 0.3, (b) 0.6, (c) 0.2

3 95%; 503·2

4 (a) 0·0027, (b) 0·0451;
£9594·60

5 (a) 0·350, (b) 364; 0·938

6 k; k^2

7 243·42; (a) 10·9%, (b) 0·68%

8 (a) 0·272, (b) 0·722

9 $\dfrac{1}{a}$; 50, 2500; 0·549; 0·301

10 0·081; 0·775; $\approx$ 65 m

11 07.13 hours

12 0·134; 3100

13 £5·34

14 1·88%

15 (a) 0·637, (b) 0·572, (c) 0·653

16 $\dfrac{1}{\lambda}$; 50·5 hours

17 0, $\dfrac{N}{12}$; 180

18 0·274; 0·083; independence of weights of males and females

19 e^{-kT_1};
$6e^{-4kT_0}(1 - e^{-kT_0})(1 - e^{-2kT_0})$

Index

Addition law   3, 4

Bayes' theorem   13, 14
Binomial distribution   37–40

Complement   1
Conditional probability   6–9
Continuity correction   66, 68
Continuous probability
   distribution   27–31
Cumulative probability function   22,
   27

Discrete probability
   distribution   21–26
Dispersion   24

Equally likely events   3
Expectation   22
Expected mean value   22
Experiment   1
Exponential distribution   52–55

Geometric distribution   41–42

Independent events   6

Markov chain   15–18
Markov process   17
Multiplication law   6, 7
Mutually exclusive events   3

Normal distribution   55–69
Normal approximation to B(n, p)
   66–68
Normal approximation to Poisson
   distribution   68, 69

Outcome   1
Outcome space   2

Poisson distribution   43–45
Probability density function (pdf)   27
Probability function   21

Random variable   21

Sample space   2
Simple event   1
Standard deviation   24

Standard normal variate   58
Standard normal distribution   57

Transition matrix   16
Tree diagram   10–12

Uniform distribution, discrete   35, 36
Uniform distribution,
   continuous   49–51

Variance   24